ALEX

KID CONCOCTIONS

Weird Wacky & Wild Stuff

You Can Make At Home!

John E. and Danita Thomas

Note to Parents

The top-secret recipes contained in this book can be made quickly, easily and best of all, very inexpensively. Kid Concoctions® encourages children to learn through creative play while reinforcing lessons in science, reading, art and mathematics. These projects are designed to increase a child's sense of pride and self-esteem. Younger children can concoct along with an adult. As the children grow, they should be encouraged to be more independent with their creations.

Because children have so much potential, we encourage you to foster creativity within them by sharing ideas and cultivating in them the desire to explore, create, learn and experiment.

Most importantly, Kid Concoctions® is a resource for spending quality time together with a child in your life. The memories you can create using Kid Concoctions® are priceless.

Happy Concocting!

John E. and Danita Thomas

CAUTION: Adult supervision is recommended for ALL projects.

 Look for the "Need Adult" icon where extra adult help is needed.

CREDITS:
Cover Design: Paula Jo Smith
Graphics & Layout: Paula Jo Smith
Illustrations: Pattie Silver-Thompson & Dooran Lee
Copy Editing: Sam Ludu & Sabre Mrkva

Published by ALEX®
251 Union Street
Northvale, NJ 07647 USA

ISBN: 098220107
Printed in China

NOTE: The information in this book is true, complete and accurate to the best of our knowledge. All suggestions and recommendations are made without guarantees on the part of the authors or the publisher. The author and publisher disclaim all liability incurred in connection with the use of this information.

KiD CONCOCTiONS®

Weird Wacky & WildStuff

You Can Make At Home!

Contents

Toy Concoctions

Contraptions

Garden Concoctions

Paints

Putties, Clays & Glues

Doughs

Edible Concoctions

Kooky Concoctions

Holiday Concoctions

NEW YEAR'S/ 99

VALENTINE'S DAY/ 101

ST. PATRICK'S DAY/ 103

More Holiday Concoctions the next page

Holiday Concoctions
continued from the previous page

4 Bonus Recipes!

Toy Concoctions

Water Balloon Yo-Yo

Try this unusual outdoor yo-yo to provide hours of fun.
It always seems to bounce right back.

WHAT YOU WILL NEED

1 small balloon   1 large rubber band

HOW TO MAKE IT

❶ Cut the rubber band in half.

❷ Tie a loop securely on one end of the rubber band. It should be big enough to fit around your finger.

❸ Use a garden hose or water faucet to fill the balloon 1/4 of the way with water.

❹ Blow air into the balloon until it is the size of a tennis ball. Tie the balloon shut.

❺ Securely tie the rubber band around the knot on the balloon.

❻ Place the rubber band loop around your middle finger and gently throw the balloon toward the ground. When the balloon springs back toward your hand, try to grab it.

PROJECT TIPS & IDEAS

✓ Use the Water Balloon Yo-Yo to put a twist on classic yo-yo tricks like Rock the Cradle and Around the World. You can also experiment and create brand new tricks of your very own.

✓ Use colored markers and stickers to decorate and personalize your Water Balloon Yo-Yo.

Sparkle Bottle

Metallic glitter is magically suspended in plastic soda bottles, creating a rainbow of swirling colors.

WHAT YOU WILL NEED

Small clear plastic soda bottle with a cap

Light corn syrup

Assorted shapes of metallic confetti (found in gift and card shops)

Cold water

HOW TO MAKE IT

❶ Fill soda bottle 3/4 of the way with corn syrup.

❷ Add a small handful of metallic confetti.

❸ Top the bottle off with water.

❹ Seal the bottle securely with a cap and shake.

PROJECT TIPS & IDEAS

✓ Add a few drops of food coloring to your Sparkle Bottle for added interest.

✓ Create Sparkle Wands by using a 1-inch diameter clear plastic aquarium lift tube (found in pet supply stores) and two 1-inch plastic chair leg caps (found in hardware stores). Secure a plastic chair leg cap on one end of the lift tube with a hot glue gun. Fill the tube with corn syrup, glitter and cold water. Glue the remaining chair leg cap on the other end of the tube and shake.

Rainbow Sand

Use this fun and inexpensive alternative to craft store art sand.

WHAT YOU WILL NEED

1 cup sand or table salt

2 tsp. powdered tempera paint

Ziplock bag

HOW TO MAKE IT

❶ Pour sand or table salt and powdered tempera paint into a ziplock bag. Shake bag for 30 seconds or until the color is evenly blended.

❷ Repeat the above step several times to create different colors of Rainbow Sand.

❸ Store leftover sand in a ziplock bag or in an airtight container.

PROJECT TIPS & IDEAS

✓ Layer different colors of Rainbow Sand in a small clear plastic soda bottle to create sand art bottles.

✓ Draw a picture or outline a picture in a coloring book using white school glue. Sprinkle different colors of Rainbow Sand over the picture to create really cool 3-D sand paintings.

Splongee Ball

This soft starburst-shaped ball is fun to play with indoors or out.

WHAT YOU WILL NEED

3 large sponges
(use 3 different colored sponges)

1 plastic cable tie

Scissors

HOW TO MAKE IT

❶ Cut each sponge into thirds lengthwise.

❷ Stack the cut sponges on top of each other in three rows of three.

❸ Grab the stack of sponges in the center and twist the stack once.

❹ Secure a plastic cable tie around the center of the twisted stack, pulling it as tight as possible.

❺ Trim the plastic cable tie down as close to the eye as possible.

PROJECT TIPS & IDEAS

✓ Use nylon sponges. They stay soft, cost less and come in a wide variety of colors.

✓ Wet your Splongee Ball and take it outside to play a splashy game of toss.

✓ Use your Splongee Ball to play soccer or volleyball.

Ocean in a Bottle

Ocean in a Bottle captures the look of rumbling ocean waves in a small bottle.

WHAT YOU WILL NEED

1 clear plastic 16 oz. soda bottle with a cap

3/4 cup light cooking oil

1/2 tbs. blue powdered tempera paint

Water

Funnel

HOW TO MAKE IT

❶ Mix oil and blue powdered tempera paint in a bowl.

❷ Let the mixture set for 10 minutes. This allows any powdered tempera paint that has not dissolved to settle at the bottom of the bowl.

❸ Using the funnel, slowly pour the oil into the plastic soda bottle. Do not pour the sediment at the bottom of the bowl into the bottle!

❹ Using the funnel, pour water into the bottle until it is full.

❺ Screw the cap on tightly. Slowly tilt the Ocean in a Bottle right to left and watch as the waves crash against the sides of the bottle.

PROJECT TIPS & IDEAS

✓ Substitute red powdered tempera paint in place of the blue to create Lava in a Bottle.

✓ Use bottles of assorted sizes and shapes to create interesting ocean/lava effects.

Sidewalk Chalk

With this concoction, you can create any size, color and shape of Sidewalk Chalk imaginable.

WHAT YOU WILL NEED

Need Adult!

1/3 cup quick-setting plaster of Paris

1 tbs. powdered tempera paint

3 tbs. water

Plastic cookie cutter, candy mold or toilet paper tube

HOW TO MAKE IT

❶ Mix plaster, powdered tempera paint and water in a small bowl until blended.

❷ Quickly spoon the mixture into a cookie cutter, candy mold or toilet paper tube sealed at one end with duct tape.

❸ Let the chalk dry 30-45 minutes.

❹ Carefully pop the chalk out of the cookie cutter or candy mold. If you are using a toilet paper tube, peel the tube away from the stick of chalk.

PROJECT TIPS & IDEAS

✓ You can create Sidewalk Chalk in a wide assortment of shapes by using different plastic molds such as ice cube trays and paper cups.

✓ Try adding 1 tsp. of glitter to the plaster before adding water to make your chalk sparkle.

Tornado in a Bottle

This simple concoction creates an amazingly realistic miniature tornado.

WHAT YOU WILL NEED

1 16 oz. clear plastic soda bottle with a cap (The more round the bottle, the better the tornado will work.)

2 drops clear liquid dish detergent

1 tsp. glitter

HOW TO MAKE IT

❶ Fill the clear plastic 16 oz. bottle with cold water.

❷ Add liquid dish detergent and glitter to the bottle.

❸ Screw the cap on tightly.

❹ Holding the bottle by the neck, turn it upside down. Quickly rotate your wrist several times in a clockwise motion. When you stop rotating your wrist, a mini-tornado will form inside the bottle.

PROJECT TIPS & IDEAS

✓ Using permanent markers, draw a picture of a city or landscape around the bottom of the plastic bottle.

✓ Add a few drops of blue food coloring to the bottle to create a sky effect.

Make-It-Yourself Stickers

Set free your creativity to make any imaginable size or shape sticker design.

WHAT YOU WILL NEED

4 tbs. hot water

2 tbs. gelatin

HOW TO MAKE IT

❶ Pour gelatin into a small glass bowl. Add hot water and stir until blended.

❷ Brush the mixture onto the back of a small picture, drawing or magazine cutout.

❸ Allow the sticker to set for 30-45 minutes or until dry.

❹ When you're ready to use your sticker, just wet the back and then stick it.

PROJECT TIPS & IDEAS

✓ Create your very own sticker album by stapling together several sheets of paper. You can then decorate the cover with crayons, markers or even your favorite stickers.

Squishy Ball

This squishy ball will stretch and mold into different shapes and sizes.

WHAT YOU WILL NEED

1 medium-size balloon

1/2 cup sand or salt

Funnel

HOW TO MAKE IT

❶ Place balloon over the end of a funnel.

❷ Pour 1/2 cup sand or salt into the funnel. If the entire 1/2 cup of filler doesn't seem to fit into the balloon, use a straw or the eraser end of a pencil to force the remaining filler into the balloon.

❸ Squeeze out any air that may have become trapped in the balloon. Tie the balloon shut.

PROJECT TIPS & IDEAS

✓ Use different filler ingredients such as cornstarch, flour or rice to give Squishy Balls a completely different feel.

✓ Squishy Balls can be used for juggling or just for playing catch with a friend.

Kooky Creepies

Here's a no-bake concoction that's very similar to an expensive toy store solution used to create rubber-like creatures.

WHAT YOU WILL NEED

1 envelope unflavored gelatin

2 tbs. hot water

2 tbs. white glue

1/2 tbs. liquid tempera paint

Assorted candy molds

HOW TO MAKE IT

❶ Mix liquid tempera paint and white glue together in a small bowl.

❷ In another small bowl, mix gelatin and hot water until the gelatin is completely dissolved.

❸ Add the gelatin/water mixture to the glue/paint mixture.

❹ Stir until the concoction begins to thicken. This can take as long as 6 to 7 minutes.

❺ When the mixture thickens, quickly pour it into a candy mold or cookie cutter.

❻ Place the mold in the freezer for 5 minutes or until firm.

❼ Carefully remove Kooky Creepies from the candy molds or cookie cutters and allow them to dry for 1 hour on each side. Store in an airtight ziplock bag.

PROJECT TIPS & IDEAS

✓ Play with Kooky Creepies just as you would any other kind of rubber-type creature.

✓ Allow Kooky Creepies to air-dry for 2-3 days and they will transform into hard plastic-like creatures.

Instant Volcano

This amazing concoction begins with a fizz, then erupts in a bubbling flow of lava.

WHAT YOU WILL NEED

2 small paper cups

1/4 cup baking soda

1/4 cup vinegar

4-6 drops red food coloring

HOW TO MAKE IT

❶ Fill the bottom of one small paper cup with 1/4 cup baking soda and set it on a plate.

❷ Place 4-6 drops of food coloring on top of the baking soda.

❸ Poke a hole, about the size of a dime, in the bottom of the second paper cup.

❹ Place the second paper cup upside down over the paper cup filled with baking soda.

❺ Pour vinegar into the hole until the volcano begins to erupt. The more vinegar you pour into the hole, the more foam the volcano will erupt.

PROJECT TIPS & IDEAS

✓ Create a fantasy volcano by adding 4-6 drops of blue or green food coloring and 1 tsp. of fine glitter to the baking soda.

✓ Use markers and paints to decorate the paper cups to look like real volcanoes.

Tubtime Crayons

With Tubtime Crayons you can color on the side of the bathtub or on tile walls and floors.

WHAT YOU WILL NEED

1 cup grated bar soap

1/4 cup warm water

4-6 drops food coloring

Plastic cookie cutters

HOW TO MAKE IT

❶ Mix water, soap and food coloring in a medium bowl. Stir the crayon mixture until it begins to stiffen.

❷ Remove the mixture from the bowl and knead it until it is the consistency of a very thick dough.

❸ Spoon crayon mixture into plastic cookie cutters.

❹ Place the plastic cookie cutters in the freezer for 10 minutes.

❺ Pop the crayons out of the cookie cutters and allow them to dry overnight or until hard.

PROJECT TIPS & IDEAS

✓ Use a plastic ice cube tray in place of cookie cutters as a mold for your Tubtime Crayons.

✓ You can also use Tubtime Crayons as bath soap.

Juggle Balls

Practice becoming a juggling expert with these clever and durable Juggle Balls.

WHAT YOU WILL NEED

1 small plastic bag

1/2 cup dried beans

2 medium-size balloons

HOW TO MAKE IT

❶ Fill a small plastic bag with dried beans until it is the size of a juggle ball.

❷ Cut the narrow end off both balloons.

❸ Stretch one balloon around the plastic bag full of dried beans.

❹ Stretch the remaining balloon around the bag in the opposite direction of the first balloon.

PROJECT TIPS & IDEAS

✓ Decorate and personalize your Juggle Balls by using assorted felt-tipped markers.

✓ Try filling your Juggle Balls with other ingredients such as dried rice, sand, or salt.

✗ Remember to remove all balloon pieces and throw them in the trash.

Comic Copier Solution

With this concoction you can make a copy of any black-and-white or colored newspaper photograph.

WHAT YOU WILL NEED

1 tsp. vanilla extract

1 tsp. liquid dish detergent

Comic strip or newspaper picture

White paper

HOW TO MAKE IT

❶ Mix vanilla extract and liquid dish detergent in a small bowl.

❷ Using your finger or a small paint brush, completely cover the comic or newspaper picture with a thin layer of Comic Copier Solution.

❸ Place a clean sheet of white paper on top of the picture. Firmly rub the back of the paper with a spoon until the picture begins to show through the paper.

❹ Peel the paper off the picture to see your Comic Copier creation.

PROJECT TIPS & IDEAS

✓ Use the Comic Copier Solution to create greeting cards and wrapping paper.

✓ Comic Copier Solution can also be used to create cool book covers or lunch bags.

Crazy Critters

You'll have hours of fun creating, decorating and naming your very own Crazy Critter pets.

WHAT YOU WILL NEED

1/3 cup quick-setting plaster of Paris

5 tbs. water

Balloons of assorted sizes

Funnel with a large opening

1 tbs. tempera paint or 5-7 drops of food coloring

Supplies to decorate critters: paint, glue, glitter, google eyes, feathers, etc.

HOW TO MAKE IT

❶ Blow up a balloon as large as possible. Clamp the end of the balloon shut with a paper clip or clothespin. Allow it to stretch for 5-10 minutes.

❷ Deflate the balloon and attach it to the funnel.

❸ Mix water, plaster and paint/food coloring until smooth. Pour plaster mixture into the balloon. Remove the funnel and tie the balloon shut.

❹ Stretch the balloon into any shape and hold it until plaster begins to become firm.

❺ Let the balloon set for 1 hour.

❻ Tear balloon off the plaster shape. Then paint or decorate your Crazy Critters.

PROJECT TIPS & IDEAS

✓ Crazy Critters make interesting and versatile conversation pieces that can be used for anything, from a paperweight to an imaginary pet.

✖ Throw balloon pieces away in the trash.

Cool Crayons

Create some of the coolest crayons you've ever seen with this simple recycling recipe.

WHAT YOU WILL NEED

Broken crayons

Heavy paper cups (microwaveble)

Assorted candy molds

Oven mitt

HOW TO MAKE IT

❶ Remove all paper from crayons and sort by color in heavy paper cups.

❷ Place one paper cup of crayons into a microwave oven. Cook on high for 4-6 minutes or until the crayons are completely melted.

❸ Have an adult use an oven mitt to carefully pour the melted crayon wax into candy molds. Throw the used paper cup away.

❹ Place the candy molds in the freezer for 20 minutes until the wax is hard.

❺ Pop Cool Crayons out of the candy molds and color.

PROJECT TIPS & IDEAS

✓ Try melting together 2-3 different colors of crayons to create marbleized crayons.

✓ If your microwave has a glass tray, let it cool down after 15 minutes of use. The tray must be allowed to cool one hour to prevent burns to the user and to prevent damage to the glass tray.

✓ Heavy paper cups must be microwave- safe.

Splongee Flyer

This flying starburst-shaped ball is fun to play with indoors or out.

WHAT YOU WILL NEED

3 small sponges
(use different colored sponges)

1 plastic cable tie

1 large rubber band

Scissors

HOW TO MAKE IT

❶ Cut each sponge into thirds lengthwise.

❷ Stack the cut sponges on top of each other in three rows of three.

❸ Grab the stack of sponges in the center and twist the stack once.

❹ Place plastic cable tie through the center of the rubber band.

❺ Secure a plastic cable tie around the center of the twisted stack, pulling it as tight as possible.

❻ Trim the plastic cable tie down as close to the eye as possible.

❼ Put the rubber band on the tip of your thumb, pull back the sponge ball and release to shoot.

PROJECT TIPS & IDEAS

✓ Use nylon sponges. They stay soft, cost less and come in a wide variety of colors.

✓ Set up targets made of decorated toilet paper tubes and try to knock them over with your Splongee Flyers.

Surprise Soaps

These ball-shaped soaps reveal secret treasures as kids wash.

WHAT YOU WILL NEED

1 cup grated bar soap

1/4 cup warm water

Food coloring

Small rubber animals or toys

HOW TO MAKE IT

❶ Mix water, soap and food coloring in a medium bowl. Stir the mixture until it begins to stiffen.

❷ Remove the mixture from the bowl and knead it until it is the consistency of a very thick dough.

❸ Roll the dough into the shape of a ball.

❹ Make a hole in the center of the ball big enough to hide treasures in.

❺ Fill the hole with treasures and seal with some extra dough.

❻ Allow Surprise Soaps to dry overnight before using.

PROJECT TIPS & IDEAS

✓ Mold the Surprise Soap dough into different shapes and sizes.

✓ Add a few drops of perfume or cologne to make scented Surprise Soaps.

Surprise Chalk

With this concoction you can create sidewalk chalk with a secret surprise inside.

WHAT YOU WILL NEED

Need Adult!

1/3 cup quick-setting plaster of Paris

1 tbs. tempera paint

3 tbs. water

Toilet paper tube

Coins, small rubber animals or toy treasures

HOW TO MAKE IT

❶ Mix plaster, powdered tempera paint and water together in a small bowl until blended.

❷ Quickly spoon half of the mixture into a toilet paper tube sealed at one end with duct tape.

❸ Place your surprise treasure in the toilet paper tube half full of the chalk mixture.

❹ Spoon the remaining chalk mixture into the toilet paper tube.

❺ Let the chalk dry 30-45 minutes.

❻ Carefully peel the toilet paper tube away from the stick of chalk.

PROJECT TIPS & IDEAS

✓ Create Surprise Chalk in different shapes by using plastic candy and soap molds.

✓ Make your Surprise Chalk sparkle by stirring 1 tsp. of glitter into the plaster mixtures.

3-D Squeeze Chalk

3-D Squeeze Chalk looks and feels like real chalk and dries in a matter of minutes.

WHAT YOU WILL NEED

1/2 cup cornstarch

2 tbs. flour

1/4 cup water

4-6 drops of food coloring

Medium-size ziplock bag

HOW TO MAKE IT

❶ Mix cornstarch and flour in a small bowl.

❷ Add water and 4-6 drops of food coloring.

❸ Mix until the consistency of a thick paste. If paste is too dry, sprinkle with a little water and stir.

❹ Pour the mixture into the ziplocklock bag and seal.

❺ Cut a small hole in the corner of the ziplock bag and squeeze the chalk out of the bag and onto the sidewalk.

PROJECT TIPS & IDEAS

✓ Put 3-D Squeeze Chalk in a disposable cake decorating bag and use different tips to create unique designs.

✓ Add 1 tsp. of glitter to make your 3-D Squeeze Chalk sparkle.

Smoke Eggs

This fun and safe concoction is a great way for kids of all ages to celebrate Independence Day.

WHAT YOU WILL NEED

Need Adult!

Eggs   Baby powder

Tape   Felt-tip markers

HOW TO MAKE IT

❶ Tap the narrow end of the egg with the back of a spoon to create a 1-inch opening.

❷ Hold the egg upside down over a bowl and shake out the contents of the egg. Wash out the eggshell and your hands with warm soapy water.

❸ Let the eggshell dry and then decorate the shell with felt-tip markers.

❹ Fill the eggshell with baby powder and then seal it with a piece of tape.

❺ Throw the egg against the driveway or sidewalk to create a smoke cloud.

❻ Clean up the mess left by the smoke eggs with a broom, a garden hose or bucket of water.

PROJECT TIPS & IDEAS

✓ Create confetti eggs for your next New Year's Eve celebration or birthday party by filling the eggshell with confetti instead of baby powder.

✓ This is an outdoor activity!

Rubber Band Ball

This goofy concoction bounces in crazy patterns and will keep you guessing what it will do next.

WHAT YOU WILL NEED

Tennis ball

Bag of multicolored rubber bands

HOW TO MAKE IT

❶ Wrap the tennis ball with a layer of rubber bands.

❷ Continue wrapping the tennis ball with rubber bands until you can no longer see the original color of the ball.

❸ The more rubber bands you add to the ball, the larger it will become.

PROJECT TIPS & IDEAS

✓ Have a contest with your friends or school classmates to see who can create the largest Rubber Band Ball.

✓ Make a Rubber Band Ball as a gift for a teacher, office worker or anyone who uses rubber bands.

Blast Ball

This original Kid Concoctions® creation will provide hours of exciting outdoor fun.

WHAT YOU WILL NEED

12-inch balloon

Woman's nylon stocking leg or knee-high stocking

Water

HOW TO MAKE IT

❶ Place the balloon inside the nylon.

❷ Put the balloon over the end of a water faucet and fill with approximately 3 tbs. of water.

❸ Blow up the balloon with air until it is 6-8 inches in diameter. Tie the balloon shut.

❹ Carefully push the balloon down into the toe area of the nylon.

❺ Tie a knot in the nylon just below the balloon, leaving a long tail.

PROJECT TIPS & IDEAS

✓ Play with your blast ball in a grassy area, keeping it away from sharp objects.

✓ Grab the Blast Ball by the tail and swing it through the air.

Contraptions

Wacky Water Cyclone

Easily create your own underwater cyclone using a few simple household items.

WHAT YOU WILL NEED

2 two-liter bottles

Plastic tape or duct tape

Water

HOW TO MAKE IT

❶ Fill one two-liter bottle 3/4 of the way full with water.

❷ Place the second bottle upside down on top of the first bottle.

❸ Securely tape the two bottles together where they meet.

❹ Turn the bottles upside down so the bottle filled with water is on top.

❺ Quickly move the bottles in a circular motion, and an underwater cyclone should appear.

PROJECT TIPS & IDEAS

✓ Add glitter or food coloring to the water before taping the two bottles together.

✓ Decorate the bottom of each bottle to look like a cityscape or farm scene.

13

Whirly Bird

This spinning helicopter-like contraption can be made quickly with just a few easy-to-find items.

WHAT YOU WILL NEED

Unsharpened pencil with eraser

Thumbtack

1-1/2-inch x 16-inch strip of thin cardboard

HOW TO MAKE IT

❶ Place the middle of the cardboard strip centered on top of the pencil eraser.

❷ Secure the cardboard strip onto the eraser of the pencil using a thumbtack.

❸ Bend each end of the cardboard strip up to form a "V" shape.

❹ Launch the Whirly Bird high into the sky by rolling the pencil between your hands and releasing it.

PROJECT TIPS & IDEAS

✓ Make your Whirly Bird more interesting by using a pencil with a unique design on it and by coloring the cardboard strip with felt-tip markers or crayons.

Crazy Compass

With this concoction, you can quickly and easily make a real working compass.

WHAT YOU WILL NEED

Sewing needle   Magnet

Tape   Wide, flat piece of cork

Plate filled with water

HOW TO MAKE IT

❶ Magnetize the needle by stroking it with a magnet repeatedly in the same direction for 30 seconds.

❷ Tape the needle to the center of the cork.

❸ Float the cork in the center of the water-filled plate.

❹ The needle will always point north and south.

needle on a cork in plate
filled with water

magnet

PROJECT TIPS & IDEAS

✓ Create a more portable compass by floating your Crazy Compass in a shallow plastic glass filled with water.

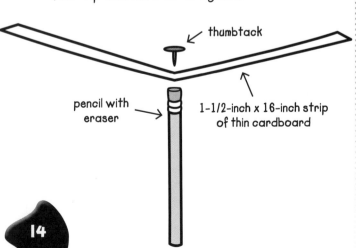

thumbtack

pencil with eraser

1-1/2-inch x 16-inch strip of thin cardboard

Pistol Popper

Children have created this classic Pistol Popper contraption for more than 100 years.

WHAT YOU WILL NEED

1-1/2-inch x 16-inch sheet of paper (cut from a brown paper bag)

HOW TO MAKE IT

❶ Fold paper in half lengthwise. Then open it back up again.

❷ Fold all 4 corners of the paper down to meet the centerfold.

❸ Fold paper in half along the centerfold.

❹ Fold paper in half and then open it back up.

❺ Fold the largest corners of the paper down. (See illustration)

❻ Fold the paper back to make a triangle shape.

❼ Make your pistol pop by holding it by the points and then snapping it down through the air.

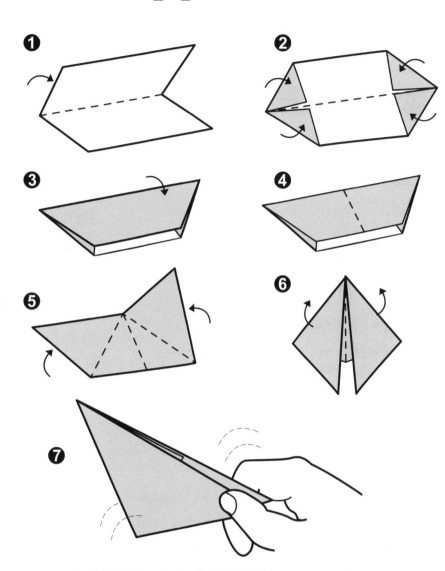

PROJECT TIPS & IDEAS

✓ Decorate your Pistol Popper using colored pencils, felt-tip markers or paints.

✓ Pistol Poppers can be a fun and inexpensive activity for birthday parties.

Uncle John's Ant Farm

You won't believe how easy it is to make this amazing ant farm with just a few household items.

WHAT YOU WILL NEED

Clear plastic 2-liter bottle with cap

Sand
(enough to fill the bottle 3/4 full)

Water

Small pin

Ants from the same colony

HOW TO MAKE IT

❶ Fill the bottle 3/4 full with sand.

❷ Pour a little water into the bottle to slightly moisten the sand.

❸ Have an adult use the pin to poke a series of air holes in the bottle.

❹ Place the ants in the bottle and screw the cap on tight.

❺ Watch as the ants begin to make tunnels.

❻ Keep the sand moist with water and feed your ants daily using bread crumbs or dead insects.

PROJECT TIPS & IDEAS

✓ Keep your ant farm out of direct sunlight.

✓ Give your ants an occasional special treat by feeding them a few drops of water and sugar mixed together.

Miniature Greenhouse

Grow plants faster and healthier with this easy-to-make Miniature Greenhouse.

WHAT YOU WILL NEED

Clear 2-liter plastic bottle

Seeds   Peat moss

Flower pot   Pebbles or small rocks

HOW TO MAKE IT

❶ Have an adult cut the plastic bottle in half. Use the top half for your greenhouse and save the bottom to create the Wacky Worm Farm (see next page).

❷ Place a handful of pebbles in the bottom of the flower pot.

❸ Fill the flower pot with peat moss and then plant your seeds.

❹ Water the soil and the seeds.

❺ Place the top half of the bottle over the flower pot and put the greenhouse in a sunny spot.

❻ Water your plant a few times a week or when the peat moss gets dry.

PROJECT TIPS & IDEAS

✓ Use brightly colored paints to decorate the flower pot and give your Miniature Greenhouse as a gift.

✓ Plant herbs in several Miniature Greenhouses to create your own indoor herb garden.

Wacky Worm Farm

With the Wacky Worm Farm, you'll have fun observing earthworms as they dig, play and eat.

WHAT YOU WILL NEED

Clear 2-liter plastic bottle

Soil

Pebbles or small rocks

Water

Sand

Fresh leaves

Earthworms

HOW TO MAKE IT

❶ Have an adult cut the plastic bottle in half. Use the bottom half for your Wacky Worm Farm and save the top to create the Miniature Greenhouse (see previous page).

❷ Layer the bottom of the bottle with pebbles.

❸ Add sand and soil in alternate layers until the bottle is almost full.

❹ Moisten the soil and sand with a little water.

❺ Lay the earthworms on top of the soil and cover them with fresh leaves.

❻ Put the Wacky Worm Farm in a dark place and keep the soil moist.

PROJECT TIPS & IDEAS

✓ Plant a few grass seeds or a mini-plant in the worm farm. Observe as the worms pull the grass or plant leaves under the soil and eat them.

Instant Intercom

Talk to your friends or family members with this homemade intercom that works just like a telephone.

WHAT YOU WILL NEED

Garden hose

Two medium-size funnels

Black electrical tape

HOW TO MAKE IT

❶ Make sure there isn't any water in the garden hose.

❷ Push a funnel in each end of the hose.

❸ Secure the funnels to the hose using black electrical tape.

❹ Test your intercom by talking into one end while holding the other end to your ear.

PROJECT TIPS & IDEAS

✓ Use colored plastic tape to decorate your instant intercom.

✓ Talk to your friends by stretching the intercom around corners, across the yard or even to a neighbor's house.

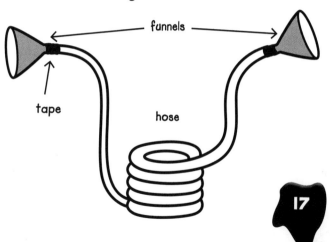

funnels

tape

hose

17

Balancing Butterfly Trick

This Balancing Butterfly Trick will amaze your friends and family as you balance the butterfly on your fingertip or nose.

WHAT YOU WILL NEED

Paper   Scissors
Cardboard   Felt-tip markers
2 small coins   Tape

HOW TO MAKE IT

❶ Fold a sheet of paper in half and draw half of a butterfly, making sure that the bottom wing is larger and hangs lower than the top wing. It is important to do this step correctly so that the butterfly will balance properly.

❷ With the paper still folded, cut out the butterfly. Trace the paper butterfly on a piece of cardboard and then cut out the cardboard butterfly.

❸ Decorate the butterfly wings with felt-tip markers.

❹ Turn the butterfly over and tape the coins to the widest part of each of the bigger wings.

❺ Balance the butterfly on your finger, your nose, the corner of a table or on the eraser of a pencil. If your butterfly does not balance, try repositioning the coins.

PROJECT TIPS & IDEAS

✓ Create a real glitzy butterfly by decorating the wings with white school glue, glitter and paint.

✓ Make several butterflies and give them as party favors.

Diving Raisins Soda

Turn a dull glass of soda pop into a mini tank of scuba-diving raisins.

WHAT YOU WILL NEED

1 glass clear soda pop
(ginger ale, club soda, etc.)
Raisins

HOW TO MAKE IT

❶ Add several raisins to the glass of clear soda pop.

❷ Watch as the raisins dive and resurface just like little scuba divers.

PROJECT TIPS & IDEAS

✓ Add 1 tsp. of baking soda to your glass of soda and the raisins will dive and resurface even faster.

Sea Monster Farm

Although they look like tiny sea monsters, these cute and amazing little creatures are actually brine shrimp.

WHAT YOU WILL NEED

1/2 tsp. brine shrimp eggs (available at your local pet store)

5 tsp. kosher salt

Fish bowl

2 quarts tap water

HOW TO MAKE IT

❶ Fill the fish bowl with 2 quarts of water. Let the water sit for 3 days. This process will allow the chlorine gas, found in most city water, to escape.

❷ Pour the salt into the water and stir until the salt is completely dissolved.

❸ Add 1/2 tsp. brine shrimp eggs to the water and then place the fish bowl in a warm spot.

❹ The eggs will begin to hatch in about 2 days. They will continue to grow for several days until they become adults.

PROJECT TIPS & IDEAS

✓ Use a magnifying glass to observe your sea monsters as they hatch from their eggs and begin to grow.

✓ Turn off the lights and then place a small flashlight next to the fish bowl. As you move the flashlight back and forth, the sea monsters will follow the light.

Bloomin' Flowers

When you place these beautiful paper flowers in a bowl of water, they begin to bloom and open up just like real flowers.

WHAT YOU WILL NEED

Construction paper   Scissors

Crayons or felt-tip markers

Small bowl of water

HOW TO MAKE IT

❶ Draw a picture of a flower on a sheet of construction paper. Use the illustration as a pattern.

❷ Color and decorate the flower, using crayons or felt-tip markers.

❸ Cut out the flower and fold shut to form a bud.

❹ Place the flower bud in a bowl of water.

❺ As the paper absorbs the water, the flower bud will open.

PROJECT TIPS & IDEAS

✓ Create your own original patterns to make Bloomin' Flowers in a wide variety of shapes and sizes.

✓ Write messages in the center of your flower. As the flower blooms, your message is revealed.

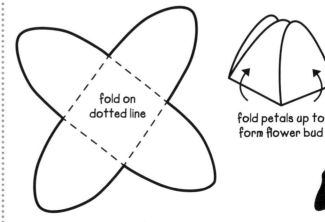

fold on dotted line

fold petals up to form flower bud

Hydro Jet Boat

This Hydro Jet Boat is actually powered by carbon dioxide gas made by mixing vinegar and baking soda.

WHAT YOU WILL NEED

Need Adult!

1 plastic 16-oz. soda bottle with cap

1/4 cup vinegar   1 tbs. baking soda

Plastic straw   White glue

HOW TO MAKE IT

❶ Ask an adult to poke a hole in the bottom edge of the plastic bottle.

❷ Insert the straw into the hole, leaving 1-inch hanging out.

❸ Seal the air cracks around the straw with white glue. Let the glue completely dry before continuing. Apply a second layer of glue, if necessary.

❹ Pour the vinegar into the bottle. Add baking soda and quickly put the cap back on the bottle.

❺ Place the Hydro Jet Boat in a tub of water and watch it go!

PROJECT TIPS & IDEAS

✓ Add a few drops of red, blue or green food coloring to the white vinegar. Observe what happens as the boat sails across the water.

✓ Make boats out of different colors of plastic bottles to create an entire fleet.

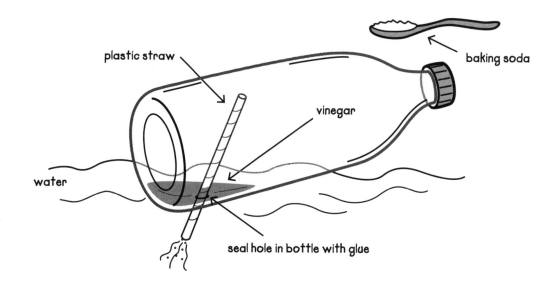

plastic straw

baking soda

vinegar

water

seal hole in bottle with glue

Ball Blaster

Launch ping pong balls across the room and into the sky using this creative ball launcher.

WHAT YOU WILL NEED

2 toilet paper tubes
Tape
1 rubber band

Ping pong balls
Plastic wrap
4 paper clips

HOW TO MAKE IT

❶ Cut one toilet paper tube lengthwise.

❷ Put the toilet paper tube back together with tape making sure it is now narrow enough to fit inside the other tube.

❸ Tape plastic wrap on one end of the narrow tube.

❹ Place the narrow tube inside of the uncut tube.

❺ Place a paper clip on the end of each tube directly across from each other.

❻ Attach one end of the rubber band to each of the paper clips (see the illustration).

❼ Place the ping pong ball inside the tube and pull the inner tube back and release it to launch the ball.

PROJECT TIPS & IDEAS

✓ Set up rows of decorated toilet paper tubes and then try to knock them over with your Ball Blaster.

✓ Decorate the ping pong balls and your Ball Blaster using felt-tip markers.

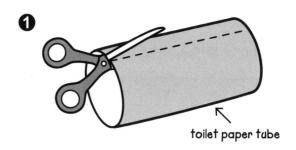

❶

toilet paper tube

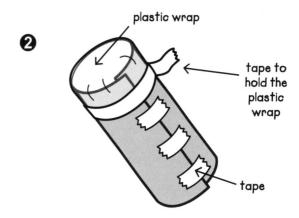

❷

plastic wrap

tape to hold the plastic wrap

tape

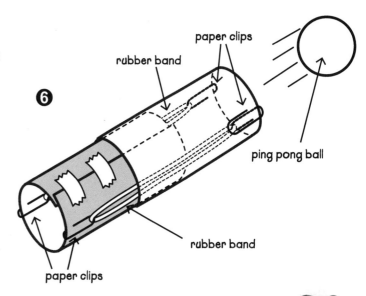

❻

paper clips

rubber band

ping pong ball

rubber band

paper clips

Rocket Slider Game

This cool Rocket Slider Game should be played with a friend who's not afraid of some fun, fast-paced rocket action.

WHAT YOU WILL NEED

Need Adult!

2 One-liter plastic soda bottles

Electrical tape

2 12-foot strings

2 plastic ring six-pack can holders

HOW TO MAKE IT

❶ Have an adult cut both plastic bottles in half.

❷ Tape the tops of both bottles together.

❸ Thread both pieces of 12-foot string through the bottles.

❹ Cut both plastic ring holders in thirds to make the 4 handles.

❺ Tie a handle to each end of the string. You're ready to play!

❻ Each player holds onto two handles and moves away from the other player until the strings are tight.

❼ Pull the strings apart to launch the rocket toward the other player. Put your hands together to allow the other player to launch the rocket toward you.

PROJECT TIPS & IDEAS

✓ Decorate the outside of your rocket using construction paper, glue and felt-tip markers.

use folded rings for each end of string

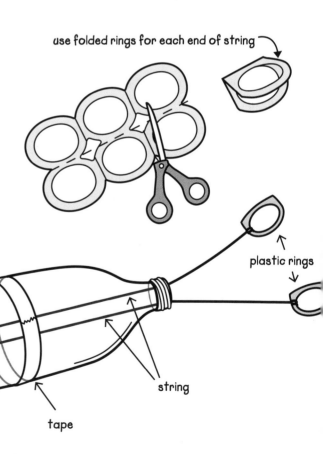

plastic rings

string

plastic rings

tape

22

Indoor Hot-Air Balloon

This amazing contraption will actually float in the air just like a real hot-air balloon.

WHAT YOU WILL NEED

Need Adult!

Tissue paper
(the kind used in gift boxes)

Glue stick

Scissors

Hair dryer

HOW TO MAKE IT

❶ Cut the sheet of tissue paper so it looks like the example shown at right.

❷ Use the glue stick to attach the angled tabs to the straight edge of the tissue. See diagram below.

❸ Use the hair dryer to inflate the balloon with hot air. After a minute or so, the balloon should float up into the air. Never let the hair dryer touch the tissue.

❹ Should your balloon begin to topple over when it starts to float, add 3 paper clips around the bottom to help weigh it down.

PROJECT TIPS & IDEAS

✓ Use colored markers to decorate your hot- air balloon.

✓ Have a contest with your friends to see whose hot-air balloon will float the highest.

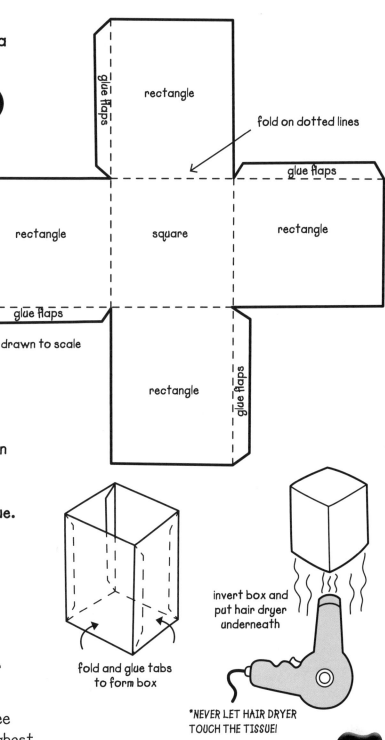

glue flaps

rectangle

fold on dotted lines

glue flaps

rectangle   square   rectangle

glue flaps

drawn to scale

rectangle

glue flaps

fold and glue tabs to form box

invert box and put hair dryer underneath

*NEVER LET HAIR DRYER TOUCH THE TISSUE!

23

Balloon Hovercraft

This balloon-powered hovercraft
will provide hours of fun.

WHAT YOU WILL NEED

Old CD

Snap cap
(from a bottle of liquid dish soap)

HOW TO MAKE IT

❶ Pull off the top of the snap cap and push
the bottom through the hole in the
center of the CD.

❷ Snap back the top of the snap cap on
the bottom, so the CD is sandwiched in-
between.

❸ Blow up the balloon and stretch it over
the closed snap cap.

❹ Pull open the snap cap and the air from
the balloon will lift the hovercraft off
the ground and make it float.

PROJECT TIPS & IDEAS

✓ Decorate your balloon with felt-tip
markers to give your hovercraft a
personalized look.

✓ Have a hovercraft race with your
friends by using drinking straws to
blow on the hovercraft and make it
shoot across the ground.

✖ Throw balloon pieces away in the trash.

❶

remove top off cap

liquid dish soap bottle cap

❷

CD

place cap bottle through hole
in CD and snap cap back on

❸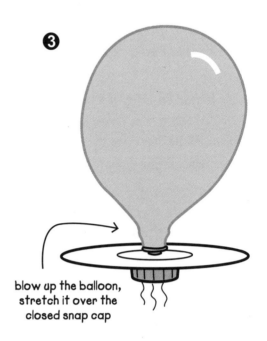

blow up the balloon,
stretch it over the
closed snap cap

24

Squeeze Rocket

Similar to the flying air rockets sold in stores—
this one costs just pennies to make!

WHAT YOU WILL NEED

Soft plastic squeeze bottle
(dishwashing liquid, ketchup
or mustard bottle works fine)

2 plastic straws,
one narrower than the other

Tape

White school glue

Paper

HOW TO MAKE IT

❶ Create your launch pad by making a hole in the
cap of the squeeze bottle and pushing the small
straw through it.

❷ Squeeze white glue around the base of the
straw to hold it in place and seal any cracks.
Let the glue dry completely and then wrap
with tape.

❸ Make your rocket by cutting 4 inches off the
larger straw.

❹ Make fins for your rocket by cutting two small
triangles out of paper and then attaching them
to the straw with tape.

❺ Seal the top of the rocket with tape. Continue
wrapping the tape around the top of the
rocket to form a nose cone.

❻ Slide the large straw (rocket) over the small
straw (launch pad) and then squeeze the bottle
hard and fast to launch the rocket into the air.

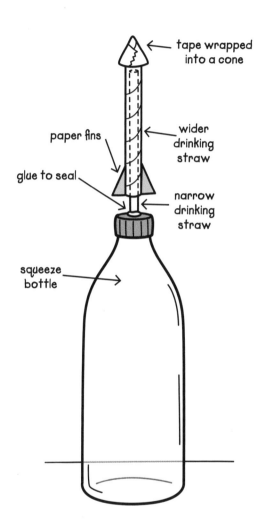

tape wrapped
into a cone

paper fins

glue to seal

wider
drinking
straw

narrow
drinking
straw

squeeze
bottle

PROJECT TIPS & IDEAS

✓ Decorate your rocket and launch
pad using paints, felt-tip markers,
or colored tape.

✓ Challenge your friends to a rocket
race to see whose rocket goes the
highest or the furthest.

Gyrocopter

Just like a helicopter, this Gyrocopter spins and then launches into the air.

WHAT YOU WILL NEED

Index card cut into a 4-inch square

Scissors   Tape

Thread spool   Thin stick

String

HOW TO MAKE IT

❶ Draw the pattern at right onto an index card.

❷ Cut on the solid lines with scissors and fold on the dotted lines as shown in the illustration. One side of each rotor should be folded up and the other down.

❸ Punch a small hole in the center of the square and push a narrow stick through it. Attach the stick firmly with tape.

❹ Push the stick in the center of the thread spool and then wrap the string around the stick.

❺ Quickly pull the string to make the Gyrocopter spin and take off into the air. You may have to try this step several times before your Gyrocopter flies.

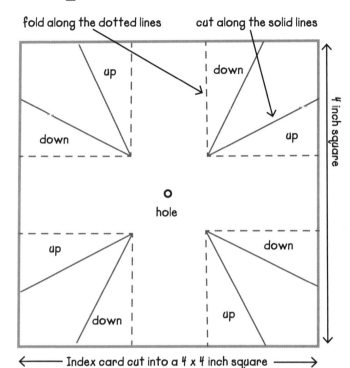

fold along the dotted lines   cut along the solid lines

up   down

down   up

o
hole

up   down

down   up

4 inch square

← Index card cut into a 4 x 4 inch square →

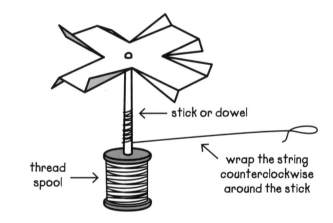

← stick or dowel

thread spool →

wrap the string counterclockwise around the stick

PROJECT TIPS & IDEAS

✓ Decorate your Gyrocopter with crayons or colored pencils.

✓ Make a bulls-eye with a piece of paper and then have a contest with your friends to see whose Gyrocopter comes closest to the center of the bulls-eye.

Balloon Retrorocket

This quick and easy contraption will keep you entertained for hours.

WHAT YOU WILL NEED

1 straw   1 oblong balloon

15 - 20 feet of string   Tape

HOW TO MAKE IT

❶ Tie one end of the string to a chair, post or tree. Thread a straw through the other end of string and pull the string as tight as possible. Tie the string to another chair, post or tree.

❷ Blow up the balloon and secure it to the straw, using two pieces of tape.

❸ Release the balloon and watch as it shoots down the line of string.

PROJECT TIPS & IDEAS

✓ Create 2 Balloon Retrorockets and have them race each other to see which one goes the furthest and the fastest.

✓ Decorate your Balloon Retrorocket with felt-tip markers.

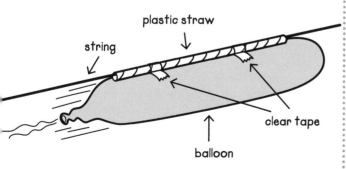

string

plastic straw

clear tape

balloon

Loopy Flyer

Children of all ages will love this simple glider which is made of two strips of paper and a drinking straw.

WHAT YOU WILL NEED

Tape   Drinking straw

1-inch x 7-inch strip of paper

3/4-inch x 6-inch strip of paper

HOW TO MAKE IT

❶ Tape the ends of each strip of paper together to form two loops, one larger than the other.

❷ Tape the small loop to one end of the straw, and the large loop to the other end of the straw.

❸ Hold the center of the straw, with the small loop facing forward and toss your Loopy Flyer into the air.

PROJECT TIPS & IDEAS

✓ Jazz up your Loopy Flyer by using colored paper to make the loops, and a bright colored straw for the body of the glider.

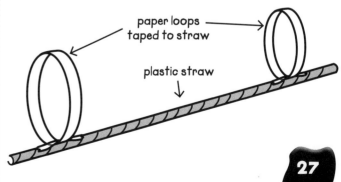

paper loops taped to straw

plastic straw

Garden Concoctions

Apple Head People

Kids of all ages will be amazed to watch big apples turn into delightful little Apple Heads.

WHAT YOU WILL NEED

1 apple

1 cup lemon juice

1/4 cup table salt

HOW TO MAKE IT

❶ Have an adult peel the apple.

❷ Draw a face on the apple using a toothpick.

❸ Have an adult carve the face, hollowing out deep eyes with a potato peeler. Then, use a paring knife to carve the nose and mouth.

❹ Roll the apple head in lemon juice and then roll it in salt.

❺ Place the apple head on a cooling or drying rack and place it in a dry location for two weeks or until it shrinks.

PROJECT TIPS & IDEAS

✓ Use markers to add color to the lips, eyes, and cheeks of your little Apple Heads.

✓ Use yarn to create hair for your Apple Heads.

Flower People

Surprise and delight unsuspecting visitors with flowers that look like people.

WHAT YOU WILL NEED

White glue

Google eyes

Pipe cleaners

Flowers
(sunflowers and large daisies work best)

HOW TO MAKE IT:

❶ Using the white glue, make two dots on the face of the flowers.

❷ Stick two google eyes onto the glue dots.

❸ Bend a pipe cleaner into the shape of a mouth. Apply glue to the back of the pipe cleaner, then stick it onto the flower.

PROJECT TIPS & IDEAS

✓ Bend green pipe cleaners around the flower stem to create arms and hands.

✓ Experiment by gluing a mouth and eyes on other types of plants besides flowers.

Flowers Forever

Dry and preserve fresh-cut flowers that will last for many years to come.

WHAT YOU WILL NEED

1 cup borax laundry booster

2 cups cornmeal

Cardboard shoebox

Fresh flowers

HOW TO MAKE IT

❶ Mix borax and cornmeal.

❷ Cover the bottom of the shoebox with 3/4-inch of the borax-cornmeal mixture.

❸ Cut the flower stems off and then place the flowers face down into the mixture as flat as possible.

❹ Pour the remaining mixture on top of the flowers until they are completely covered.

❺ Place the lid on top of the shoebox and set it in a dry place at room temperature for 3-4 weeks.

❻ Remove dried flowers from the shoe box.

PROJECT TIPS & IDEAS

✓ Flowers that have great drying results include: daisies, pansies, apple blossoms, asters and violets.

Living Words

Plant seeds and they grow into words and pictures that will amaze your friends and family.

WHAT YOU WILL NEED

Grass seed

Potting soil

3-4-inch deep dish

Pencil

HOW TO MAKE IT

❶ Fill the dish with 2-3 inches of potting soil.

❷ Moisten the soil with a plant mister.

❸ Use a pencil or stick to write words or draw a picture in the soil.

❹ This will create little trenches to plant the seeds in.

❺ Carefully sprinkle grass seed into trenches made with the pencil.

❻ Gently cover the seeds with a thin layer of soil and moisten with the plant mister.

❼ Lightly moisten the soil 1-2 times a day with the plant mister. Your Living Words will begin to sprout in 7-10 days.

PROJECT TIPS & IDEAS

✓ Use chive seeds instead of grass seed to create Living Words.

✓ Try planting Living Words outside in the garden.

Painted Carnations

Create beautiful Painted Carnations, using household ingredients and a little bit of science.

WHAT YOU WILL NEED

White carnations

6-8 drops food coloring

HOW TO MAKE IT

❶ Cut carnation stems at an angle 5 inches away from the flower.

❷ Fill a glass or small vase with 3 inches of water and stir in 6-8 drops of food coloring.

❸ Place each flower in a different color of water.

❹ After 24 hours, the tips of the flower petals will have a light tint of color. The longer the flowers are left in the colored water, the brighter the color will be.

PROJECT TIPS & IDEAS

✓ Create a bouquet of brightly colored flowers to make a beautiful Painted Carnation centerpiece.

Egg Head Garden

This wild and crazy garden concoction is sure to plant a smile on your face.

WHAT YOU WILL NEED

Eggs

Potting soil

Grass seed, flower seeds, or herb seeds

Felt-tip markers

HOW TO MAKE IT

❶ Hollow the eggs out by tapping the small end against a hard surface to create a 1-inch hole on top of the egg.

❷ Remove the contents of each egg by shaking it over a bowl.

❸ Draw a face on your egg head using felt-tip markers.

❹ Spoon each egg full of potting soil.

❺ Make a small hole in the soil with a pencil.

❻ Place a few seeds in the hole, cover with soil and water.

❼ Depending on the type of seeds used, your Egg Head Garden will sprout in 7-10 days.

PROJECT TIPS & IDEAS

✓ By transplanting your Egg Head Garden outside, you can enjoy it all summer long.

Greenhouse in a Bag

This nifty concoction is a great way to see how seeds sprout and grow.

WHAT YOU WILL NEED

Small ziplock bag

3 wet cotton balls

2-3 large seeds (beans work best)

Clear tape

HOW TO MAKE IT

❶ Place the wet cotton balls in the ziplock bag with the seeds placed against them.

❷ Seal the ziplock bag and tape it to a window where it will receive plenty of sunlight. Your seed should begin to sprout in 3-5 days.

❸ After your sprouts grow at least 1 inch, you can transplant it in soil so that the plant may continue to grow.

PROJECT TIPS & IDEAS

✓ Make several Greenhouses in a Bag using different types of seeds. Observe the seeds to see which ones sprout first and how fast they grow.

Bean Mosaics

Create festive and colorful mosaic pictures using dried beans and a little imagination.

WHAT YOU WILL NEED

White glue

Dried beans (lima, pinto, black, kidney, etc.)

Heavy paper or cardboard

Pencil

HOW TO MAKE IT

❶ Use a pencil and draw a picture on a heavy sheet of paper or cardboard

❷ Use white glue to fill in a small area of the picture.

❸ Immediately cover the glue with the beans. Repeat the process until the entire picture is completed.

PROJECT TIPS & IDEAS

✓ Use Bean Mosaics to decorate the front of greeting cards, picture frames and small boxes.

✓ Light color beans can be stained by painting them with the following mixture: 1 tbs. water and 3-4 drops food coloring.

Magic Candle Art

Layers of colored wax create this unique and unusual candle.

WHAT YOU WILL NEED

Pieces of old used candles separated by color

Kitchen grater

Candlewick

Baby food jar (with the label removed)

HOW TO MAKE IT

❶ Have an adult grate the candle pieces into a fine powder.

❸ Layer different colors of the candle powder in a baby food jar.

❸ Gently push a candlewick into the center of the jar.

PROJECT TIPS & IDEAS

✓ Try making Magic Candles in different types of glass containers such as jelly and pickle jars.

✓ Decorate the outside of your Magic Candle with colorful stickers to create a wonderful gift for any holiday.

✓ Magic Candles should be lit and supervised by an adult. Never use a glass container with a rim that hangs over the wick. This can cause the container to crack or break.

Frosted Glass Candles

Create the look and feel of real frosted glass using salt and nail polish.

WHAT YOU WILL NEED

Table salt

Assorted colors of nonflammable nail polish

Baby food jar

HOW TO MAKE IT

❶ Remove the label from the baby food jar.

❷ Paint a design on the outside of the baby food jar using different colors of nail polish.

❸ Sprinkle salt on top of the nail polish while it is still wet.

❹ Let your finished candleholder dry overnight.

❺ Place a small votive inside the baby food jar. Candles should be lit and supervised by an adult.

PROJECT TIPS & IDEAS

✓ Use clear nail polish to create the look of white frosted glass.

Apple Candleholders

This old-fashioned concoction is the perfect way to turn fresh fruit into elegant candleholders.

WHAT YOU WILL NEED

Apple

Apple corer

1 cup lemon juice

Candle

HOW TO MAKE IT

❶ Use the apple corer to remove the core from the apple.

❷ Soak the apple in lemon juice for 2 minutes.

❸ Insert the candle into the cored apple.

❹ The candle should be lit and supervised by an adult.

❺ Throw away the apple after the candle burns down. Do not eat it!

PROJECT TIPS & IDEAS

✓ Use different colors of apples to create your Apple Candleholders.

✓ Push cloves into the outside of the apple to create different designs.

Ice Lanterns

Light up a dark winter's night with these warm, inviting crystal Ice Lanterns.

WHAT YOU WILL NEED

Need Adult!

Large plastic bowl

Plastic yogurt container full of stones or coins.

HOW TO MAKE IT

❶ Place 2 inches of water into the large plastic bowl and freeze.

❷ Place the yogurt container full of stones or coins in the center of the frozen ice bowl.

❸ Pour more water into the bowl until it almost reaches the rim of the yogurt container and freeze.

❹ Run warm water over the outside of the plastic bowl and the ice bowl should pop out.

❺ Remove the stones or coins from the yogurt container and pour in warm water. Remove the yogurt container when it becomes loose.

❻ Have an adult put a small votive candle in the opening left by the yogurt container and place it outside. The candle should be lit only by an adult.

PROJECT TIPS & IDEAS:

✓ Create Ice Lanterns in a wide variety of colors by mixing a few drops of food coloring with the water before freezing it.

Paints

Scratch & Sniff Watercolors

With Scratch & Sniff Watercolors, you can paint pictures of oranges that smell like oranges, grapes that smell like grapes, and cherries that smell like cherries.

WHAT YOU WILL NEED

1 tbs. unsweetened powdered drink mix

1 tbs. warm water

Several small containers (muffin tins work well)

HOW TO MAKE IT

❶ Mix water and unsweetened drink mix in a small bowl. Repeat this step several times, using various flavors of drink mix to create different colors of paint.

❷ Allow finished works to dry overnight before scratching and sniffing.

PROJECT TIPS & IDEAS

✓ Use Scratch & Sniff Watercolors along with the Make-It-Yourself Stickers recipe on page 5 to create your very own Scratch & Sniff stickers.

✓ Create unique Scratch & Sniff greeting cards and wrapping paper.

35

Bathtub Finger Paints

You'll have fun finger painting while getting yourself and the tub clean at the same time.

WHAT YOU WILL NEED

1/3 cup clear mild liquid dish detergent

1 tbs. cornstarch

Food coloring

HOW TO MAKE IT

❶ Mix liquid dish detergent and cornstarch together in a small bowl until blended.

❷ Pour the mixture, in equal parts, into several sections of a plastic ice cube tray.

❸ Add 1-2 drops of food coloring to each section of the tray and mix with a small spoon.

PROJECT TIPS & IDEAS

✓ Use Bathtub Finger Paints on the inside of the bathtub to paint pictures and even play games such as hangman and tic-tac-toe.

✓ Bathtub Finger Paints also work well as a traditional finger paint.

Super Sidewalk Paint

Now you can color large portions of sidewalk space in just a fraction of the time it would take with traditional stick chalk.

WHAT YOU WILL NEED

1/4 cup cornstarch

1/4 cup cold water

6-8 drops food coloring

HOW TO MAKE IT

❶ Mix cornstarch and cold water in a small plastic bowl.

❷ Add food coloring and stir.

❸ Repeat this process to create different colors of Super Sidewalk Paint. Super Sidewalk Paint can be washed away easily with water.

PROJECT TIPS & IDEAS

✓ Super Sidewalk Paint is great for painting rainbows or other pictures where large areas of color are needed.

✓ Use Super Sidewalk Paint for painting hopscotch grids, cakewalks, even make-believe roads and highways for toy cars.

Puddin' Paint

Budding young artists will enjoy this wonderful "first paint."

WHAT YOU WILL NEED

1 large package of instant vanilla pudding (3.4 oz)

2 cups ice-cold water

Food coloring

HOW TO MAKE IT

❶ Whisk water and instant pudding in a bowl for 2 minutes.

❷ Refrigerate for 5 minutes.

❸ Divide pudding into several small bowls or muffin tins.

❹ Add 5-7 drops of food coloring to each bowl or tin, and mix.

PROJECT TIPS & IDEAS

✓ Use Puddin' Paints along with other paints in this book to create really cool works of art. Puddin' Paints also double as a fantastic finger paint!

Tattoo Paint

This rich, creamy paint allows you to create colorful, removable tattoos.

WHAT YOU WILL NEED

1 tbs. cold cream

2 tbs. cornstarch

1 tbs. water

Food coloring

HOW TO MAKE IT

❶ Mix cold cream and cornstarch in a small bowl. Stir in water. Continue stirring until the mixture is smooth.

❷ Divide the mixture into 3 or 4 small plastic bowls.

❸ Mix 3-4 drops of food coloring into each bowl.

❹ Apply Tattoo Paint, using a small paintbrush or cotton swab.

❺ Remove paint with soap and water.

PROJECT TIPS & IDEAS

✓ Use Tattoo Paint to create removable tattoos on your arms, legs, or face.

✓ Tattoo Paint works well when used in conjunction with Face & Body Paint to create Halloween or masquerade characters.

Magic Bubble Paint

Use this concoction to create and capture bright, colorful bubble prints.

WHAT YOU WILL NEED

2 tsp. clear liquid dish detergent

3 tbs. water

1/4 cup powdered tempera paint

HOW TO MAKE IT

❶ Mix clear liquid dish detergent, water, and powdered tempera paint in a small, shallow bowl. If you are using concentrated dish detergent, 1-2 more tbs. of water may be necessary.

❷ Using a straw, gently blow into the paint mixture until a dome of bubbles forms.

❸ Capture the bubble print by placing a piece of paper on top of the bubble dome.

❹ Repeat the process, using several different colors of bubble paint.

PROJECT TIPS & IDEAS

✓ Use Magic Bubble Paint to create custom stationery, envelopes, greeting cards, wrapping paper, photo mats, and cool lunch bags.

✓ Layer different colors of Magic Bubble Paint to create a swirling "marble-like" effect.

I Can't Believe It's Not Oil Paint

Here's a concoction that captures the look and feel of real oil paint without the expense or mess!

WHAT YOU WILL NEED

2 tbs. clear liquid dishwashing detergent

2 tbs. powdered tempera paint

1/2 tsp. water

HOW TO MAKE IT

❶ Pour liquid detergent, powdered tempera paint, and water into a small bowl or container.

❷ Mix the ingredients until they are completely blended.

❸ I Can't Believe It's Not Oil Paint can be stored for several weeks at room temperature in an airtight container.

PROJECT TIPS & IDEAS

✓ Mix different colors of I Can't Believe It's Not Oil paint to create your own unique custom-blended paints. Think of names to call all the new colors you've created, even silly names like Orangutan Orange or Stoplight Red.

Foamy Paint

Foamy paint is not just great for painting on paper. You can also use it to paint on tile floors and walls.

WHAT YOU WILL NEED

1 can white shaving cream

Food coloring

Plastic ice cube tray or muffin tin

HOW TO MAKE IT

❶ Place a small dab of shaving cream into several ice cube tray or muffin tin sections.

❷ Add 1-2 drops of food coloring to each section, and mix with a small spoon.

PROJECT TIPS & IDEAS

✓ Use Foamy Paint to create 3-D foam sculptures.

✓ Foamy Paint can be used to paint pictures on your arms and legs.

Instant Finger Paints

With this quick and easy concoction, you can duplicate commercial-quality finger paints.

WHAT YOU WILL NEED

1/4 cup liquid starch

1 tbs. powdered tempera paint

Freezer paper (Paint on the shiny side.)

HOW TO MAKE IT

❶ Pour liquid starch and powdered tempera paint into a small bowl.

❷ Mix until well blended.

❸ Use plastic margarine or yogurt tubs with lids to store finger paints for future use.

PROJECT TIPS & IDEAS

✓ Create pictures of all your favorite people, places, and things. You may even want to challenge a friend or family member to a game of Instant Finger Paint tic-tac-toe!

✓ Use a brush to paint with Instant Finger Paints just as you would any other paint.

Face & Body Paint

Here's a wonderful face and body paint that is very similar to store-bought grease paint makeup.

WHAT YOU WILL NEED

2 tbs. solid shortening

1 tbs. cornstarch

4-5 drops food coloring

Small makeup sponges

HOW TO MAKE IT

❶ Mix shortening and cornstarch in a small bowl until smooth.

❷ Add 4-6 drops of food coloring. Mix until the color is evenly blended.

❸ Apply Face & Body Paint to arms, legs and face using a small makeup sponge.

❹ Remove paint with soap and water.

PROJECT TIPS & IDEAS

✓ Children can use Face & Body Paint to transform themselves into green spacemen, yellow goblins or even circus clowns.

✓ Add 1 tsp. of glitter to Face & Body Paint to create sparkle makeup.

Jiggle Finger Paints

This great-smelling concoction shimmers, shakes, and tickles your fingertips as you paint.

WHAT YOU WILL NEED

1 package (3 oz.) flavored sugar-free gelatin

2 tbs. hot water

Freezer paper (Paint on the shiny side.)

HOW TO MAKE IT

❶ Mix gelatin and water in a small bowl.
Do not overmix!

❷ Let Jiggle Finger Paints cool 5-10 minutes before using.

❸ Jiggle Finger Paints will dry completely in 24 hours.

PROJECT TIPS & IDEAS

✓ You can create unscented Jiggle Finger Paints by mixing 1 package of unflavored gelatin with 2 tbs. of hot water and 4-6 drops of food coloring.

Instant Watercolors

Here's one of the quickest, easiest and least expensive watercolor recipes you will ever find.

WHAT YOU WILL NEED

5-7 drops food coloring

2 tbs. water

HOW TO MAKE IT

❶ Mix water and food coloring in a small container until completely blended.

❷ Repeat the above process to create different colors of paint.

PROJECT TIPS & IDEAS

✓ Use Instant Watercolors as you would any other type of watercolor paint.

Easy Egg Marbleizing

This concoction lets you create beautiful marbleized eggs in just minutes.

WHAT YOU WILL NEED

1 tbs. food coloring

1 tbs. vinegar

1 tbs. cooking oil

Hard-boiled eggs

Water

HOW TO MAKE IT

❶ Combine food coloring, oil and vinegar in a small bowl until blended.

❷ Add enough water to make the liquid deep enough to cover an egg.

❸ Swirl the liquid around with a spoon. Quickly lower an egg into the solution and remove.

❹ Pat the egg dry with a paper towel.

❺ Repeat the above process using a different color of food coloring.

❻ Leave a little bit of oil on the egg to give it a varnished look.

PROJECT TIPS & IDEAS

✓ Draw a design on your egg with a white crayon before dipping. The dye will not stick to your design.

✓ Use hollow eggs that have been blown out instead of hard-boiled eggs.

Fantastic Finger Paint

This classic finger paint recipe is the perfect rainy-day concoction.

WHAT YOU WILL NEED

1 cup flour

2 tbs. salt

1-1/2 cups cold water

1-1/4 cups hot water

Food coloring

Freezer paper (Paint on the shiny side.)

HOW TO MAKE IT

❶ Combine flour, salt and cold water in a saucepan. Beat with a wire whisk until smooth.

❷ Heat the mixture over medium heat. Slowly stir in hot water.

❸ Continue stirring until the mixture boils and begins to thicken. Remove from heat.

❹ Beat with a whisk until smooth.

❺ Divide the mixture into several different containers. Add 4-5 drops of food coloring to each container and stir.

PROJECT TIPS & IDEAS

✓ Finger paint without getting your hands messy by placing a piece of plastic wrap over freezer paper with the finger paint between the layers.

✓ Finger paint on plastic bowls and cups. It's lots of fun and when you're finished the paint washes away.

3-D Puffy Sand

Create unique 3-D paintings that dry to a rock-like finish.

WHAT YOU WILL NEED

1/3 cup flour

1/3 cup water

1/3 cup salt

2-1/2 tbs. tempera paint

1/2 tbs. sand

Plastic squeeze bottle

HOW TO MAKE IT

❶ Combine dry ingredients in a medium bowl.

❷ Add water and tempera paint. Mix until well blended.

❸ Carefully pour the mixture into a plastic squeeze bottle.

❹ Let finished 3-D Puffy Sand paintings dry 24 hours or until hard.

PROJECT TIPS & IDEAS

✓ Place 3-D Puffy Sand into a cake-decorating bag and use different tips to create cool effects and textures.

✓ Use 3-D Puffy Sand to decorate picture frames, jewelry boxes, lunchboxes and greeting cards.

Spray Chalk

This washable spray paint works on sidewalks, in the snow or on the sand.

WHAT YOU WILL NEED

4 tbs. cornstarch

1 cup warm water

4-6 drops food coloring

1 small plant mister

HOW TO MAKE IT

❶ Mix all ingredients in a medium bowl.

❷ Pour the Spray Chalk mixture into a small plant mister. Shake and spray.

❸ Avoid clogging by shaking the plant mister before each use.

PROJECT TIPS & IDEAS

✓ Use Spray Chalk at the beach to paint colorful sand sculptures, on sidewalks to create graffiti-type art or in the snow to create dazzling winter rainbows and colorful snowmen.

Poster Paint

This bright-colored paint is wonderful for painting posters, signs and banners.

WHAT YOU WILL NEED

1/4 cup flour

1 cup water

3 tbs. powdered tempera paint

1/2 tsp. liquid starch

HOW TO MAKE IT

❶ Mix flour and water in a saucepan. Stir until smooth.

❷ Heat over low heat until the mixture begins to thicken. Remove from heat and let cool.

❸ Pour the mixture into a small bowl. Add powdered tempera paint and liquid starch. Stir until completely blended.

❹ Store poster paint in an airtight container.

PROJECT TIPS & IDEAS

✓ Poster Paint works well on cardboard and paper surfaces. You can even use it to paint papier-mâché sculptures.

✓ Give Poster Paint a pleasant scent by adding 1 tbs. of peppermint or any other extract.

Glossy Paint

Create a quality high-gloss paint in just seconds using common kitchen ingredients.

WHAT YOU WILL NEED

1/2 cup condensed milk

6-8 drops food coloring

HOW TO MAKE IT

❶ Mix condensed milk and food coloring in a small bowl until completely blended.

❷ Repeat the above process several times to create different colors of Glossy Paint.

PROJECT TIPS & IDEAS

✓ Glossy Paint can also be used as a high-gloss finger paint.

✓ Use 1 tbs. of liquid tempera paint in place of food coloring to create Glossy Paint in even brighter colors.

44

Wacky Watercolors

This concoction begins with a fizz and eventually becomes hard cakes of watercolor paint.

WHAT YOU WILL NEED

3 tbs. baking soda

3 tbs. cornstarch

3 tbs. white vinegar

1-1/2 tsp. light corn syrup

Food coloring

HOW TO MAKE IT

❶ Mix vinegar, baking soda, cornstarch and corn syrup together in a small bowl.

❷ Divide the mixture into several small plastic tubs or jar lids.

❸ Add 6-8 drops of food coloring to each tub or lid and mix.

❹ Use Wacky Watercolors as they are or allow them to dry into hard cakes of paint. When painting with dry paint cakes, be sure to wet your brush before painting.

PROJECT TIPS & IDEAS

✓ Experiment by mixing different colors of food coloring to create custom-blended colors of Wacky Watercolors.

✓ Use Wacky Watercolors with a pencil and a coloring book to create your own paint-by-number pictures.

Snow Paint

With Snow Paint you can have fun creating colorful pictures and designs in the snow without harming the environment.

WHAT YOU WILL NEED

1 cup water

10-12 drops food coloring

1 small plant mister

HOW TO MAKE IT

❶ Pour water into a small plant mister.

❷ Add 10-12 drops of food coloring. Screw back the spray top on the plant mister and shake.

❸ Repeat the above process to create Snow Paint in a variety of colors.

PROJECT TIPS & IDEAS

✓ Make a snowman or a snow angel. Then use Snow Paint to create faces and clothing for your snow creations.

✓ Use Snow Paint to create messages or banners in the snow.

Sticky Paint

Sticky Paint's smooth texture and rich color make it the perfect paint for very young artists.

WHAT YOU WILL NEED

2 tbs. light corn syrup

4-6 drops food coloring

HOW TO MAKE IT

❶ Mix corn syrup and food coloring in a small bowl until well blended.

❷ Repeat the above process to create different colors of Sticky Paint.

PROJECT TIPS & IDEAS

✓ Sticky Paint also makes a wonderful finger paint.

✓ Substitute 1 tsp. of liquid tempera paint in place of food coloring to create even more vivid colors.

45

Snowy Foam Paint

Snowy Foam Paint looks like real snow and dries to a plastic foam-like finish.

WHAT YOU WILL NEED

1 cup white school glue
1 cup white shaving cream

HOW TO MAKE IT

❶ Mix shaving cream and glue in a small bowl.

❷ Let the mixture set for 2 minutes.

❸ Use a brush to paint with Snowy Foam Paint.

PROJECT TIPS & IDEAS

✓ Add a few drops of food coloring to Snowy Foam Paint and create colorful pictures.

✓ Dip foam balls into Snowy Foam Paint to create snowmen and other snow-like sculptures.

Marble Paint

You'll have fun while painting amazing works of art with marbles.

WHAT YOU WILL NEED

Marbles
2 tbs. liquid tempera paint
Plastic cup
Large shallow pan or pie tin
Paper

HOW TO MAKE IT

❶ Pour tempera paint into the plastic cup.

❷ Gently drop 3-4 marbles into the paint.

❸ Place a sheet of paper inside the pan so that it is laying flat on the bottom.

❹ Spoon out the paint-covered marbles from the plastic cup and into the pan.

❺ Tilt the pan side to side to create your Marble Paint design. Let the paint dry before handling the paper.

PROJECT TIPS & IDEAS

✓ Use Marble Paint to create greeting cards, wrapping paper, party invitations and stationery.

✓ Try using different colors of paint on the same sheet of paper to create interesting designs.

Bath & Body Paint

With this wild concoction you can paint your body and get clean at the same time.

WHAT YOU WILL NEED

1/4 cup liquid baby bath

1 tbs. cornstarch

2-3 drops food coloring

Plastic ice cube tray

HOW TO MAKE IT

❶ Mix liquid baby bath and cornstarch until blended.

❷ Pour the mixture into a plastic ice cube tray.

❸ Add 2-3 drops of food coloring to each section and paint.

PROJECT TIPS & IDEAS

✓ Use a paintbrush to paint your body and the side of the bath tub.

✓ Bath & Body Paint also makes a great finger paint when used on wax paper.

Freeze Pop Paint

Budding young artists will enjoy painting with these frozen paint pops.

WHAT YOU WILL NEED

2 tsp. powdered tempera paint

1/3 cup water

Wax-coated paper cup

Craft sticks

Plastic wrap

HOW TO MAKE IT

❶ Mix powder tempera paint and water.

❷ Pour the mixture into a wax-coated paper cup.

❸ Cover the cup with plastic wrap, then insert a craft stick through the plastic wrap into the center of the cup.

❹ Place the cup in the freezer and freeze until solid.

❺ Remove the paper cup and plastic wrap from the Freeze Pop Paint.

❻ Dip the Freeze Pop Paint into water and paint on white paper.

PROJECT TIPS & IDEAS

✓ Make Freeze Pop Paint in a plastic ice cube tray instead of a wax paper cup.

✓ Use Freeze Pop Paint to create cool wrapping paper and greeting cards.

Super Spray Paint

This homemade spray paint is great for painting cool pictures, large signs and banners.

WHAT YOU WILL NEED

1 tbs. powder tempera paint

1 cup water

Spray bottle

HOW TO MAKE IT

❶ Mix paint and water in a small bowl.

❷ Pour the mixture into a spray bottle and paint.

❸ Shake the Super Spray Paint bottle before each use.

PROJECT TIPS & IDEAS

✓ Add 1 tbs. of white school glue to your Super Spray Paint to make it shiny.

3-D Popcorn Paint

Use 3-D Popcorn Paint just like you would use paint or crayons to color your favorite pictures.

WHAT YOU WILL NEED

1 cup popped popcorn

2 tbs. water

5-7 drops food coloring

Large ziplock bag

White school glue

HOW TO MAKE IT

❶ Pour popcorn into a large ziplock bag.

❷ Mix food coloring and water and then pour the mixture on top of the popcorn.

❸ Seal the ziplock bag and shake it until the popcorn changes color.

❹ Pour the popcorn out onto a paper towel to dry.

❺ Use popcorn paint by filling the area you want to color with school glue and then cover the glue with the popcorn paint. Let the picture dry for 24 hours before moving or hanging it.

PROJECT TIPS & IDEAS

✓ Use 3-D Popcorn Paint to create unique greeting cards and decorate gift boxes.

✓ Make interesting ornaments and mobiles by cutting shapes out of cardboard and covering them with 3-D Popcorn Paint. Hang up your ornament or mobile by poking a hole through it and then tying a piece of string or yarn through the hole.

Goofy Glass Paint

This project works just like expensive store-bought glass paints.

WHAT YOU WILL NEED

1/4 cup white school glue

1/4 cup liquid tempera paint

HOW TO MAKE IT

❶ Mix glue and tempera paint in a small bowl.

❷ Use a paintbrush to apply Goofy Glass Paint to the surface you wish to paint.

❸ Let painted items dry overnight before using.

❹ Dried Goofy Glass Paint can be removed by an adult using a razor blade.

PROJECT TIPS & IDEAS

✓ Give new life to old vases and jars by painting them with Goofy Glass Paint.

✓ Remove the label from an old peanut butter jar and paint it with Goofy Glass Paint to create a really cool pencil-and-pen holder.

Magic Paint

Your friends will be amazed when you send them an invisible message using Magic Paint.

WHAT YOU WILL NEED

1 tbs. baking soda

2 tbs. water

4-6 drops food coloring

Paintbrush

Paper

HOW TO MAKE IT

❶ Mix 1 tbs. water and 1 tbs. baking soda together.

❷ Dip your paintbrush into the baking soda/water mixture and then write your mystery message on a sheet of paper.

❸ Let the message completely dry.

❹ To reveal your Magic Paint message, mix the remaining 1 tbs. of water and 4-6 drops of food coloring.

❺ Using a brush, paint the water and food coloring mixture over the Magic Paint message. Your message will be revealed.

PROJECT TIPS & IDEAS

✓ Try making a Magic Paint greeting card for a birthday or any other special occasion.

✓ Paint a Magic Paint picture to give to a friend or family member.

Fruity Finger Paints

With this quick and easy concoction you can make fruity-scented commercial-quality finger paints.

WHAT YOU WILL NEED

2 cups flour

2 tbs. (2 envelopes) unsweetened drink mix

1/2 cup salt

3 cups hot water

3 tbs. cooking oil

Freezer paper (Paint on the shiny side.)

HOW TO MAKE IT

❶ Mix flour, drink mix and salt.

❷ Stir in water and cooking oil.

❸ Paint on the shiny side of the freezer paper.

PROJECT TIPS & IDEAS

✓ Challenge a friend or family member to a game of Fruity Finger Paint hangman or tic-tac-toe!

✓ Use a brush to paint with Fruity Finger Paints just as you would any other paint.

Crystal Paint

This amazing paint actually crystallizes as it dries.

WHAT YOU WILL NEED

1/8 cup liquid starch

1/8 cup water

4-6 drops food coloring

HOW TO MAKE IT

❶ Mix liquid starch and water in a small bowl.

❷ Stir in food coloring.

❸ Use a brush to apply Crystal Paint to paper.

PROJECT TIPS & IDEAS

✓ Use Crystal Paint to create unique holiday greeting cards, banners and wrapping paper.

Salty Paint

This concoction lets you turn regular table salt into beautiful, sparkling works of art.

WHAT YOU WILL NEED

2 tbs. table salt

1/2 tbs. powder tempera paint

White school glue

Ziplock bag

HOW TO MAKE IT

❶ Pour salt and tempera paint into the ziplock bag and shake.

❷ Repeat the above process to create Salty Paint in different colors.

❸ Draw a picture on a sheet of paper using the white school glue.

❹ Sprinkle the Salty Paint on top of the glue, then carefully shake off any excess salt.

❺ Let the Salty Paint dry overnight before you touch it.

PROJECT TIPS & IDEAS

✓ Pour different colored layers of Salty Paint into an old baby food jar to create faux sand art.

✓ Give your Salty Paint a little more pizzazz by mixing in 1 tsp. of glitter.

Glitter Paint

This wacky paint dries to a shiny, transparent finish.

WHAT YOU WILL NEED

1/4 cup corn syrup

4-6 drops food coloring

1 tbs. glitter

HOW TO MAKE IT

❶ Mix corn syrup and food coloring in a small container. Slowly stir in glitter to avoid clumping.

❷ Use a brush to paint on a sheet of paper.

❸ Let your finished Glitter Paint pictures dry for 24 hours.

PROJECT TIPS & IDEAS

✓ Use Glitter Paint to create beautiful pictures of rainbows and starry night skies.

✓ Omit the food coloring from the paint mixture to create clear Glitter Paint.

Milky Way Paint

This cool Kid Concoctions® paint looks like a creamy pastel color when it dries.

WHAT YOU WILL NEED

1/2 cup powder nonfat milk

1/2 cup water

6-8 drops food coloring

HOW TO MAKE IT

❶ Mix milk, water and food coloring in a small bowl.

❷ Repeat the above step several times to create different colors of Milky Way Paint.

❸ Milky Way Paint dries in 1-2 hours.

❹ Do not store Milky Way Paint or let it set out longer than a few hours.

PROJECT TIPS & IDEAS

✓ Milky Way Paint is super for painting pictures of sunsets, skies, oceans and lakes.

✓ Milky Way Paint makes a great "first paint" for young children.

Whipped Cream Finger Paint

This delicious finger paint is a fun way to introduce small children to finger painting.

WHAT YOU WILL NEED

1/4 cup whipped cream

2-4 drops food coloring

Freezer paper

HOW TO MAKE IT

❶ Mix whipped cream and food coloring in a small bowl. Repeat this step to create various different colors of Whipped Cream Finger Paint.

❷ Finger paint on the shiny side of the freezer paper. Freezer paper works just as well as store-bought finger painting paper and it's a lot less expensive.

PROJECT TIPS & IDEAS

✓ Add a drop of vanilla, peppermint or banana extract to give Whipped Cream Finger Paint a wonderful scent and a great taste.

Salt Crystal Paint

With this cool concoction you can create sparkling pictures made of real crystals.

WHAT YOU WILL NEED

1/4 cup very warm water

3 tsp. salt

Paintbrush

Black paper

HOW TO MAKE IT

❶ Mix water and salt in a small bowl until salt is almost dissolved.

❷ Use a paintbrush to paint a picture using the salt mixture on a black sheet of paper.

❸ As the painting begins to dry, white sparkling crystals will begin to appear.

PROJECT TIPS & IDEAS

✓ Add a few drops of food coloring to your Salt Crystal Paint and create sparkling colorful pictures.

✓ Use Salt Crystal Paint to decorate holiday cards and wrapping paper.

Bubbling Brew Finger Paints

This wacky brew of foaming, bubbling finger paints will amaze kids of all ages.

WHAT YOU WILL NEED

Solution A

1 tbs. white vinegar

1 tbs. clear liquid dish soap

4 drops food coloring

Solution B

1 tbs. baking soda

1 tbs. water

HOW TO MAKE IT

❶ Mix vinegar, dish soap and food coloring in a small bowl. (Solution A)

❷ In another bowl, mix baking soda and water. (Solution B)

❸ Pour Solution B into Solution A. The paint will begin to bubble and foam instantly.

❹ Stir the mixture until the color is even and then paint.

PROJECT TIPS & IDEAS

✓ Try painting on the shiny side of inexpensive freezer paper. It works just as well as store-bought finger painting paper.

✓ Make magic color-change finger paints by coloring Solution A with red food coloring and Solution B with yellow food coloring. When you mix the solutions together, the paint will be orange.

Magic Marble Dip

Use this crafty concoction to create beautiful marbleized paper, envelopes and other items.

WHAT YOU WILL NEED

Oil-based enamel paints
(model car & airplane paint works best)

Paper

Disposable aluminum cake or lasagna pan

Toothpick

Water

Rubber gloves

HOW TO MAKE IT

❶ Fill a disposable aluminum pan with 3 inches of water.

❷ Pour 1 tsp. of oil-based paint into the water. Repeat this step using 2-3 other colors of paint.

❸ Swirl the colors of paint with a toothpick.

❹ Put on your rubber gloves and quickly dip a sheet of paper into the water and then slowly pull it back out. The paper should be marbleized.

❺ Let the sheet of paper dry for 24 hours.

PROJECT TIPS & IDEAS

✓ Try dipping other items such as pens, pencils and small objects into the marbleizing solution.

✓ Make an entire marbleized stationery set that includes paper, envelopes and a pencil or pen.

Wacky Window Paint

This washable paint is perfect for creating awesome works of art on windows and large glass doors.

WHAT YOU WILL NEED

2 tbs. clear liquid dish soap

1 tbs. poster paint or liquid tempera paint

Paintbrushes

HOW TO MAKE IT

❶ Mix liquid dish soap and paint in a small bowl.

❷ Repeat the above step using several different colors of paint.

❸ Dip your brush into the Wacky Window Paint and paint on a glass window or glass door. Be careful not to get paint on woodwork, caulking or any other non-glass surface.

PROJECT TIPS & IDEAS

✓ Remove Wacky Window Paint by wiping with a moist paper towel or old cloth.

✓ Use Wacky Window Paint to create window decorations for holidays throughout the year.

Rain Paint

Turn a rainy day into a fun day by actually painting with raindrops.

WHAT YOU WILL NEED

Paper plate (uncoated)

Food coloring

HOW TO MAKE IT

❶ Place several drops of food coloring on the plate.

❷ Have an adult place the plate outside in the rain for 10 - 60 seconds. Time will vary depending on how fast the rain is falling.

❸ Bring the plate indoors to dry.

PROJECT TIPS & IDEAS

✓ Try drawing a picture on the plate with a white crayon before adding food coloring.

✓ Experiment by substituting washable poster paint or tempera paint for food coloring.

Natural Plant Paints

Create your own natural paints, just like the ones used in ancient times, using various different types of plants.

WHAT YOU WILL NEED

Grass for green

Carrots for orange

Cranberries for pink

Dandelions or daffodils for yellow

Beets for red

Water

HOW TO MAKE IT

❶ Have an adult boil each of the plants in a separate pot of water until the water turns to the desired shade or color.

❷ Remove the water from heat and allow it to cool.

❸ Separate your Natural Plant Paints into small paper cups or muffin tins and paint.

PROJECT TIPS & IDEAS

✓ Experiment by making paints from spices (mustard, curry, red currants, paprika and cocoa) mixed with a little bit of water.

Putties, Clays & Glues

Funny Putty

This stretchy, rubbery putty bounces like a ball and picks up newspaper comics.

WHAT YOU WILL NEED

1 tbs. liquid starch

2 tbs. white glue

2-3 drops food coloring

Plastic Easter egg or ziplock bag

HOW TO MAKE IT

❶ Mix white glue and food coloring together in a small bowl.

❷ Pour liquid starch into a second small bowl.

❸ Slowly pour the glue mixture on top of the liquid starch.

❹ Allow the concoction to stand for 5 minutes or until the glue absorbs the liquid starch.

❺ Remove putty from bowl and knead.
(Note: At first this mixture may look as if it's a mistake, but it isn't. The more you knead the putty, the better the consistency will be.)

❻ Store Funny Putty in a plastic Easter egg or ziplock bag.

PROJECT TIPS & IDEAS

✓ Press Funny Putty down on newspaper comics or pictures printed with an ink jet printer. Slowly pull the Funny Putty off the paper. The picture will transfer magically onto the putty.

✓ Roll your Funny Putty into a ball and bounce it!

Gooey Gunk

This slimy, stretchy, gooey recipe has become one of the most popular concoctions of all time.

WHAT YOU WILL NEED

Need Adult!

Solution A

1 cup water

1 cup white glue

2 tbs. liquid tempera paint or 7-10 drops food coloring

Solution B

1-1/3 cups warm water

4 tsp. borax laundry booster

HOW TO MAKE IT

❶ Mix ingredients in Solution A in a medium-sized bowl.

❷ In a second medium-sized bowl, mix the ingredients in Solution B until the borax is completely dissolved.

❸ Slowly pour Solution A into Solution B (Do not mix).

❹ Roll Solution A around in Solution B 4-5 times.

❺ Lift Solution A out of Solution B and knead for 2-3 minutes. Store Gooey Gunk in an airtight container or ziplock bag.

PROJECT TIPS & IDEAS

✓ Use red liquid tempera paint/food coloring to create Lava Gunk, green to create Slimy Gunk or black to create Tar Gunk.

Magic Muck

This mysterious concoction is tranformed from a liquid into a solid and back again.

WHAT YOU WILL NEED

3/4 cup cornstarch

1/3 cup water

5-7 drops food coloring

HOW TO MAKE IT

❶ Mix water and food coloring together in a small bowl.

❷ Slowly add cornstarch to water and food coloring mixture. Do not stir.

❸ Let the mixture stand for 2-3 minutes.

❹ Pick up a handful of Magic Muck and squeeze it until it forms a hard ball. Open your hand and the Magic Muck will turn from a solid ball back into a liquid.

PROJECT TIPS & IDEAS

✓ Experiment by adding different proportions of water and cornstarch.

✓ Add a little glitter to make your Magic Muck sparkle.

Paper Clay

Paper Clay is a fabulous molding compound that will allow you to sculpt and mold using real paper.

WHAT YOU WILL NEED

2 cups construction paper scraps (sorted by color)

4-1/2 cups water

1/2 cup flour

HOW TO MAKE IT

❶ Tear construction paper into small pieces. Pour water and paper scraps into a blender. Blend 20 seconds or until the mixture turns into pulp.

❷ Drain and squeeze excess water from the mixture.

❸ Mix flour and the remaining 1/2 cup of water in a small bowl until blended.

❹ Slowly add the flour and water mixture to paper pulp. Knead until it forms a dough.

❺ Mold Paper Clay as you would any clay or dough. Let finished creations dry 1-2 days.

PROJECT TIPS & IDEAS

✓ Paper clay can be used to create 3-D greeting cards, pictures, package ties or tree ornaments.

✓ Try adding glitter or bits of confetti to your Paper Clay.

✓ Press Paper Clay into candy molds, cookie cutters or gelatin molds to create interesting shapes.

Cotton Clay

With this concoction you can create snowmen and other snow-like sculptures all year around.

WHAT YOU WILL NEED

3 cups cotton balls

2 cups water

2/3 cup flour

5-7 drops food coloring

HOW TO MAKE IT

❶ Tear cotton balls into small pieces. Mix water and cotton in a medium saucepan.

❷ Slowly stir in flour. Continue stirring and cook over low heat for 5-7 minutes until the mixture begins to stiffen.

❸ Remove saucepan from heat and place the Cotton Clay on a thick cloth towel or several layers of paper towels to cool.

❹ After sculpting, allow Cotton Clay sculptures to dry 24 hours or until hard.

PROJECT TIPS & IDEAS

✓ Use Cotton Clay to create 3-D holiday snow sculptures.

✓ Cotton Clay can also be used like papier-mâché. Try molding some Cotton Clay around small boxes, bottles, and balloons.

Papier-Mâché Paste

This classic concoction recipe has been a favorite of children for many years.

WHAT YOU WILL NEED

1 cup cold water

1/4 cup flour

5 cups water

HOW TO MAKE IT

❶ Mix flour and 1 cup of water in a small bowl until smooth.

❷ Heat 5 cups of water in a large saucepan over medium heat until the water begins to boil.

❸ Add flour and water mixture to boiling water. Continue to boil, while constantly stirring for 3-5 minutes.

❹ Remove pan from heat and allow Papier-Mâché Paste to cool.

❺ Dip strips of newspaper in Papier-Mâché Paste and place them over some type of mold or form (i.e., balloon or box).

❻ Allow finished Papier-Mâché Paste sculptures to dry overnight or until hard.

PROJECT TIPS & IDEAS

✓ Try making a piñata, recipe on page 108.

✓ Make beads, treasure boxes, animals and more with Papier-Mâché Paste. Then paint your creations.

Oatmeal Play Clay

Oatmeal Play Clay's interesting texture provides a unique sculpting experience for kids of all ages.

WHAT YOU WILL NEED

1/2 cup flour

1/2 cup water

1 cup oatmeal

HOW TO MAKE IT

❶ Combine flour, water and oatmeal together in a medium bowl.

❷ Stir until the mixture is smooth. If the dough is too sticky, add more flour.

❸ Remove Oatmeal Play Clay from the bowl and place it on a floured surface.

❹ Knead dough for 3-4 minutes. Store in an airtight container.

PROJECT TIPS & IDEAS

✓ Make different colors of Oatmeal Play Clay by stirring 6-8 drops of food coloring into the dough mixture.

✓ Oatmeal Play Clay is the perfect dough recipe for a young child's first sculpting experience.

Jewel & Gem Goop

Mold this strange concoction into sparkling creations that look just like real jewels and gems.

WHAT YOU WILL NEED

1/2 cup white glue

2 cups rock salt

6-8 drops food coloring

HOW TO MAKE IT

❶ Mix rock salt and food coloring. Add glue and continue mixing for 2-3 minutes.

❷ Mold and sculpt Jewel & Gem Goop with your hands.

❸ Place Jewel & Gem sculptures on a piece of cardboard to dry. Drying time will vary according to the size and thickness of your creation.

PROJECT TIPS & IDEAS

✓ Spoon Jewel & Gem Goop into plastic cookie cutters to create sparkling gems in a wide variety of shapes and sizes.

✓ Use Jewel & Gem Goop to create sparkling jewelry, holiday ornaments or even make-believe secret treasures.

Crafty Clay

Crafty Clay is perfect for creating detailed pieces such as beads and small figures.

WHAT YOU WILL NEED

1 cup cornstarch

1-1/4 cups cold water

2 cups baking soda

HOW TO MAKE IT

❶ Combine cornstarch and baking soda in a small saucepan.

❷ Add water and stir until the mixture is smooth.

❸ Heat mixture for 5 minutes over medium heat. Stir until it begins to thicken and turns to dough.

❹ Remove dough from saucepan and allow it to cool.

❺ Knead dough 2-3 minutes. Let finished creations air-dry until hard.

PROJECT TIPS & IDEAS

✓ Add color to your Crafty Clay by mixing in 7-10 drops of food coloring before cooking.

✓ Knead in 1 tsp. of fine glitter to make your Crafty Clay sculptures sparkle.

Sand Castle Clay

With this concoction you can create sand castles and sand sculptures that are permanent.

WHAT YOU WILL NEED

1 cup sand

1/2 cup cornstarch

3/4 cup liquid starch

HOW TO MAKE IT

❶ Combine sand and cornstarch in an old pot.

❷ Add liquid starch and mix.

❸ Cook the mixture over medium heat while constantly stirring. Eventually, the mixture will thicken and turn into dough.

❹ Remove pot from the stove and let Sand Castle Clay cool.

❺ Remove clay from the pot and knead it 20-30 seconds before using. Let Sand Castle Clay sculptures dry until hard.

PROJECT TIPS & IDEAS

✓ Color Sand Castle Clay by adding 1 tbs. of powdered tempera paint to the mixture before cooking.

✓ Use candy molds and cookie cutters to shape Sand Castle Clay.

Super School Glue

This homemade concoction is an inexpensive alternative to store-bought school glue.

WHAT YOU WILL NEED

3/4 cup water

2 tbs. corn syrup

1 tsp. white vinegar

1/2 cup cornstarch

3/4 cup ice-cold water

HOW TO MAKE IT

❶ Mix water, corn syrup and vinegar in a small saucepan until smooth.

❷ Heat the mixture over medium heat until it reaches a rolling boil.

❸ In a small bowl, mix cornstarch and cold water. Slowly add this mixture to the first mixture. Stir until well blended.

❹ Remove saucepan from heat and allow the glue to cool.

❺ Let the glue set overnight before using. Store in an airtight container.

PROJECT TIPS & IDEAS

✓ Use Super School Glue as you would use any store-bought school glue.

✓ Add a little pizzazz to your Super School Glue by mixing in 4-6 drops of food coloring.

Flower Petal Clay

Flower Petal Clay is a beautiful, natural clay that you can use to create small treasures in a rainbow of swirling colors.

WHAT YOU WILL NEED

1/2 cup flour

1 tbs. salt

3 tbs. water

3 cups finely chopped and crushed fresh flower petals

HOW TO MAKE IT

❶ Mix flour, salt and water in a small bowl until it forms a firm dough.

❷ Knead in flower petals.

❸ Wrap dough in plastic wrap and put it in the refrigerator for 20 minutes. Now you're ready to create!

❹ Let finished pieces air-dry 2-3 days or until completely hard. You can apply a thin layer of shellac to preserve and add luster to your Flower Petal Clay creations.

PROJECT TIPS & IDEAS

✓ With Flower Petal Clay, you can create beautiful beads in many shapes and sizes. Use a toothpick to poke a hole in your beads while they are still wet. After your beads are dried, you can string them to form unique bracelets, necklaces or tree garlands.

Spray Glue

This is a great easy way to make your own spray adhesive and shellac.

WHAT YOU WILL NEED

3/4 cup water

1/4 cup white school glue

Spray bottle

HOW TO MAKE IT

❶ Mix glue and water together in a small bowl until blended.

❷ Pour the mixture into the spray bottle.

❸ Shake the mixture well before each use.

PROJECT TIPS & IDEAS

✓ Add a few drops of food coloring to create colored Spray Glue.

✓ Use Spray Glue to put a shiny finish on dried clay sculptures or to stick large pieces of paper together.

Dryer Lint Clay

This velvet-like dough is a great way to recycle old dryer lint.

WHAT YOU WILL NEED

3 cups dryer lint

2 cups warm water

2/3 cup wheat flour

HOW TO MAKE IT

❶ Mix all ingredients in a large saucepan.

❷ Have an adult cook the mixture over low heat, stirring constantly until the mixture starts to hold together.

❸ Pour the mixture out onto several layers of newspapers to cool.

❹ Dryer Lint Clay dries to a hard, smooth finish.

PROJECT TIPS & IDEAS

✓ Shape the Dryer Lint Clay over bottles, boxes, and balloons.

Toothpaste Putty

With Toothpaste Putty you can have fun creating beads and colorful sculptures that dry hard as a rock.

WHAT YOU WILL NEED

1 tbs. white school glue

2 tbs. cornstarch

1/2 tbs. water

1/2 tbs. toothpaste

1-2 drops food coloring

HOW TO MAKE IT

❶ Mix glue, cornstarch, food coloring and toothpaste together in a small bowl.

❷ Add water and stir until the mixture turns into a clump of putty.

❸ Toothpaste Putty must be used very quickly. It will begin to harden in 25 minutes or less and will be completely dry in 24 hours.

PROJECT TIPS & IDEAS

✓ Push Toothpaste Putty into candy molds to create sculptures in a wide variety of shapes and sizes.

Doughs

Peanutty Play Dough

Here's a great dough for sculpting edible works of art.

WHAT YOU WILL NEED

1/4 cup peanut butter
1/2 cup nonfat dry milk
1/2 tbs. honey
Ziplock bag

HOW TO MAKE IT

❶ Pour peanut butter, dry milk and honey into a ziplock bag.

❷ Close the bag and knead until the mixture turns to dough.

❸ Do not reuse or store Peanutty Play Dough.

PROJECT TIPS & IDEAS

✓ Use Peanutty Play Dough to create a wide variety of edible sculptures including animals, flowers and even dinosaurs.

✓ Use raisins and assorted candies to add eyes, mouths and other features to your edible creations.

✓ Be sure to eat your creations right away!

Woody Wood Dough

With this amazing concoction you can create and mold real wood sculptures in just a few minutes.

WHAT YOU WILL NEED

1 cup clean, well-sifted sawdust

1/2 cup flour

1 tbs. liquid starch

1 cup water

HOW TO MAKE IT

❶ Mix ingredients in a bowl until a stiff dough is formed. Add extra water if dough is too dry.

❷ Allow Woody Wood Dough to dry 2- 3 days. Sandpaper can be used to smooth Woody Wood Dough after it is completely dry.

PROJECT TIPS & IDEAS

✓ Press Woody Wood Dough into cookie cutters and candy molds to create paperweights, beads and tree ornaments.

✓ Finished pieces can be painted or stained with a mixture of food coloring and water (6 drops of food coloring to 1 tbs. of water).

Plastic Dough

This stretchy, moldable dough quickly dries to a hard, plastic-like consistency.

WHAT YOU WILL NEED

4-6 drops food coloring

1/4 cup white glue

1/2 cup flour

1/2 cup cornstarch

1/4 cup water

HOW TO MAKE IT

❶ Mix white glue, water and food coloring in a small bowl until well blended.

❷ Combine flour and cornstarch in a separate bowl.

❸ Add the flour/cornstarch mixture to the water/glue mixture. Mix until a stiff dough is formed.

❹ Remove dough from the bowl and knead it on a floured surface for 2-3 minutes.

❺ Mold Plastic Dough on a surface covered with wax paper. Drying time will vary according to the size and thickness of your creation.

PROJECT TIPS & IDEAS

✓ Plastic Dough can be used to create a wide variety of items, including beads, jewelry, paperweights, bookmarks or anything else your imagination will allow.

Java Dough

This silky-smooth dough smells like fresh-brewed coffee and dries to an antique finish.

WHAT YOU WILL NEED

1/4 cup instant coffee

Need Adult!

3/4 cup warm water

2 cups flour

1/2 cup salt

HOW TO MAKE IT

❶ Mix water and instant coffee until the instant coffee is dissolved.

❷ Combine flour and salt in a medium bowl.

❸ Add the coffee mixture and stir until a smooth dough is formed.

❹ Bake finished sculptures in the oven at 300 degrees for 30-45 minutes or until hard.

❺ Store extra dough in an airtight container or ziplock bag.

PROJECT TIPS & IDEAS

✓ Use 3/4 cup of warm coffee instead of water for an even more fragrant dough.

✓ Preserve your Java Dough sculpture by adding 1-2 coats of shellac.

Coffee Dough

This concoction dries to an antique stone-like finish and is great for making small sculptures.

WHAT YOU WILL NEED

1 cup coffee grounds

Need Adult!

1 cup flour

1 cup salt

1 cup water

HOW TO MAKE IT

❶ Mix coffee grounds, flour and salt in a small bowl.

❷ Add water and stir until the mixture turns into the consistency of stiff clay.

❸ If the clay is too sticky, knead in more flour.

❹ Let Coffee Dough sculptures air-dry or bake them in the oven at 200 degrees for 45 minutes. Larger sculptures may take longer to dry.

PROJECT TIPS & IDEAS

✓ Make Coffee Dough beads to create a necklace or bracelet that will dry to a stone-like finish.

Salty Map Dough

Here is the perfect recipe for creating landscapes, school diaramas and sculptures.

WHAT YOU WILL NEED

1-1/2 cups flour

1-1/2 cups salt

1-1/8 cups water

Tempera paints (optional)

HOW TO MAKE IT

❶ Mix flour and salt in a large bowl.

❷ Slowly stir in water until the mixture is the consistency of bread dough.

❸ Salty Map Dough should be used immediately.

❹ Allow your finished Salty Map Dough creations to dry for 48 hours.

PROJECT TIPS & IDEAS

✓ Create the ultimate salt map by using 3-D Puffy Sand (page 42) to create details such as rivers, lakes and mountains.

✓ Use assorted colors of tempera paints to paint your salty landscape.

Fruity Play Dough

This soft, pliable play dough is as much fun to smell as it is to sculpt and mold.

WHAT YOU WILL NEED

2-1/4 cups flour

1 cup salt

2 tbs. unsweetened powdered drink mix

4 tbs. cooking oil

1 cup water

HOW TO MAKE IT

❶ Combine flour, salt and powdered drink mix in a large bowl.

❷ Stir in cooking oil and water.

❸ Continue stirring until mixture is the consistency of bread dough.

❹ Remove dough from bowl and knead it on a floured surface 2-3 minutes until firm.

PROJECT TIPS & IDEAS

✓ Mold different Fruity Play Dough colors/scents into pieces of make-believe fruit. Just make sure you don't eat them!

✓ Store leftover Fruity Play Dough in an airtight container or ziplock bag.

Sticky Bread Dough

This is a wonderful dough that kids can use to create ornaments, beads, and sculptures.

WHAT YOU WILL NEED

4 slices of white bread
(with the crusts cut off)

4 tbs. of white school glue

4-6 drops food coloring

HOW TO MAKE IT

❶ Break the bread into small pieces and place in a bowl.

❷ Add white school glue and food coloring.

❸ Stir until blended.

❹ Knead the mixture with your hands until it forms a soft dough.

❺ Sculpt with the Sticky Bread Dough and allow it to dry overnight until hard.

PROJECT TIPS & IDEAS

✓ Roll out the Sticky Bread Dough on wax paper and cut different shapes with cookie cutters to make ornaments and gift tags.

✓ Use 1 tbs. of coffee instead of food coloring to give Sticky Bread Dough an antique-like finish.

Crepe Paper Dough

This fun concoction is a creative way to recycle crepe paper after a party or celebration.

WHAT YOU WILL NEED

1 roll crepe paper

1/2 cup flour

1/4 cup salt

Large bowl of water

HOW TO MAKE IT

❶ Tear the roll of crepe paper into small pieces and soak it in a large bowl of water overnight until it turns into pulp.

❷ Drain the water off the pulp.

❸ Measure one packed cup of pulp into a bowl.

❹ Mix in flour and salt.

❺ Knead the mixture with your hand until it turns into a dough. If the dough is too sticky, add more flour.

PROJECT TIPS & IDEAS

✓ Use Crepe Paper Dough to create beautiful tie-dye- like beads for bracelets and necklaces.

✓ Mold Crepe Paper Dough around a small tin can to create a beautiful vase for fresh flowers.

Super Soapy Dough

You'll have hours of fun creating, molding, and squeezing this great-smelling dough.

WHAT YOU WILL NEED

2 cups flour

1/2 cup salt

1 tbs. liquid soap

6-8 drops food coloring

Water

HOW TO MAKE IT

❶ Mix flour, salt, liquid soap, and food coloring together in a small bowl.

❷ Slowly add water until a workable dough is formed. The amount of water will vary, depending on the brand of liquid soap used.

❸ If the dough becomes too sticky, add a little more flour.

❹ Mold with Super Soapy Dough just as you would any other type of dough or clay.

PROJECT TIPS & IDEAS

✓ Add a little color to your Super Soapy Dough by adding 4-6 drops of food coloring to the ingredients before mixing.

Potato Dough

We came up with this wacky dough while figuring out what to do with leftover mashed potatoes.

WHAT YOU WILL NEED

2 cups mashed potatoes

1 1/2 cups flour

4-6 drops food coloring

HOW TO MAKE IT

❶ Mix mashed potatoes and flour in a large bowl.

❷ Add 4-6 drops of food coloring and stir until the color is evenly blended.

❸ Use Potato Dough as you would any other type of dough. Do not store or reuse Potato Dough.

PROJECT TIPS & IDEAS

✓ Add a few drops of extract or 1 tbs. of unsweetened drink mix to give Potato Dough a wide variety of scents and colors. If you're using drink mix, omit food coloring from the concoction.

Edible Concoctions

Rock Candy

This tasty, homemade treat has been a favorite of children around the world for many decades.

WHAT YOU WILL NEED

Need Adult!

2 cups water   4 cups sugar

HOW TO MAKE IT

❶ Pour water into a large saucepan.

❷ Add sugar and stir for 2-3 minutes to dissolve as much sugar as possible.

❸ Place the saucepan on the stove on medium to medium-high heat.

❹ Continue to stir the solution until all the sugar is dissolved.

❺ Remove the saucepan from the stove and allow the liquid to cool.

❻ Pour the mixture into a square plastic container.

❼ In 7-10 days the bottom of your container will be covered with Rock Candy.

❽ Turn the plastic container upside down in a sink and allow it to drain for one hour.

❾ Break the Rock Candy into chunks and place them on several layers of paper towels to dry.

PROJECT TIPS & IDEAS

✓ Before cooking, add food coloring to your sugar mixture to create edible Rock Candy gems that look like rubies, emeralds and sapphires.

✓ Layer different colors of Rock Candy in a jar to create a colorful candy art gift.

Doggy Treats

Now you can easily create cool and tasty treats that your favorite canine friend will love.

WHAT YOU WILL NEED

2 cups whole wheat flour

1/4 cup cornmeal

1/2 cup Parmesan cheese (divided in half)

1 medium egg

1 cup water

HOW TO MAKE IT

❶ Mix all ingredients together, reserving 1/4 cup of the Parmesan cheese. Knead until thoroughly mixed.

❷ Roll the dough mixture into 3-inch pencil-sized sticks.

❸ Roll the Doggy Treats into the rest of the Parmesan cheese.

❹ If you are making stick-shaped treats, twist the sticks 3-4 times. Then place the treats on an ungreased baking sheet.

❺ Bake at 350 degrees for 25-30 minutes.

❻ Store Doggy Treats in an airtight container. One batch yields 18-20 small treats.

PROJECT TIPS & IDEAS

✓ Use cookie cutters to create Doggy Treats in the shape of animals or dog bones.

✓ Knead in 8-10 drops of food coloring to add variety to your Doggy Treats.

Shake & Make Ice Cream

Prepare this ice-cold, tasty treat in just a few minutes.

WHAT YOU WILL NEED

2 tbs. sugar

1 cup milk or half-and-half

1/2 tsp. vanilla

6 tbs. rock salt

1 pint-sized ziplock bag

1 gallon-sized ziplock bag

HOW TO MAKE IT

❶ Fill the gallon-size ziplock bag half full with ice. Add rock salt and seal.

❷ Pour sugar, milk (or half-and-half) and vanilla into the pint-sized ziplock bag and seal.

❸ Place the pint-size ziplock bag into the gallon-size ziplock bag and seal.

❹ Shake the bag for 5-7 minutes.

❺ Open the small ziplock bag and enjoy.

PROJECT TIPS & IDEAS

✓ Make peppermint ice cream by adding 1/2 tsp. peppermint extract or 3 tbs. of crushed peppermint stick.

✓ Try topping your ice cream with sprinkles, nuts or fresh fruit.

Candy Clay

Not only can you sculpt with this awesome clay, you can eat it!

WHAT YOU WILL NEED

1 pound powdered sugar

1/3 cup corn syrup

1/2 tsp. salt

1/3 cup margarine (softened)

1 tsp. vanilla extract

5-7 drops food coloring

HOW TO MAKE IT

❶ Mix all ingredients together in a small bowl until blended. If the mixture is too sticky, add more powdered sugar.

❷ Sculpt with your Candy Clay to create different animals, pretend fruits and other sculptures you can eat!

PROJECT TIPS & IDEAS

✓ Experiment by using different colors and different flavors of extract (banana, almond, etc.).

✓ Use Candy Clay sculptures to decorate the top of your favorite dessert.

Crazy Pretzels

Create soft, tasty pretzels in different crazy shapes and sizes.

WHAT YOU WILL NEED

Need Adult!

1 package yeast

1 tbs. sugar

1-1/2 cups warm water

4 cups flour

1 tsp. salt

1 egg, beaten

HOW TO MAKE IT

❶ Mix warm water and yeast together in a large bowl until the yeast dissolves.

❷ Add salt, sugar and flour.

❸ Mix and knead the dough until it is smooth.

❹ Roll and twist the dough into letters, numbers and animal shapes.

❺ Lay the pretzels on a greased cookie sheet, brush with a beaten egg, then lightly sprinkle with extra salt.

❻ Bake at 425 degrees for 12 to 15 minutes.

PROJECT TIPS & IDEAS

✓ Add a few drops of food coloring to the Crazy Pretzel dough to create rainbow-colored pretzels.

Shake & Make Butter

Have a blast creating tasty butter in minutes by shaking a ziplock bag full of kitchen ingredients.

WHAT YOU WILL NEED

1 large ziplock bag or plastic container with lid

1 pint heavy whipping cream

1 pinch of salt

HOW TO MAKE IT

❶ Pour heavy whipping cream and salt into the large ziplock bag or container.

❷ Seal the ziplock bag or container.

❸ After 15 minutes of shaking, chunks of butter will start to form.

❹ Drain excess liquid from the bag or container then reseal.

❺ Store the butter in the refrigerator until you are ready to use it.

PROJECT TIPS & IDEAS

✓ Push Shake & Make Butter chunks into a candy mold, place them in the refrigerator and pop them out when hard.

✓ Add 1 tbs. of honey or maple syrup to add more flavor to your Shake & Make Butter.

Chocolate Bowl

This tasty chocolate bowl makes the perfect dessert when served full of ice cream or fresh fruit.

WHAT YOU WILL NEED

1 small balloon

1 cup semisweet chocolate chips

HOW TO MAKE IT

❶ Pour chocolate chips into a microwaveable bowl and place in the microwave for 5 minutes on the medium setting. Remove from microwave and stir.

❷ Keep repeating the above process until the chocolate chips are melted.

❸ Blow up and tie the balloon, then dip it half way into the melted chocolate.

❹ Let the balloon cool 3-4 minutes and then re-dip in the melted chocolate.

❺ Repeat step 4 until a thick layer of chocolate covers the balloon.

❻ Let the chocolate cool for 1 hour and then pop the balloon using a pin.

PROJECT TIPS & IDEAS

✓ Fill your Chocolate Bowl with pudding, ice cream, fresh fruit or your favorite dessert.

✖ Remember to remove all balloon pieces and throw them in the trash.

73

Edible Ocean

This tasty treat is great for birthday parties and is sure to amaze kids of all ages.

WHAT YOU WILL NEED

4 cups premade blueberry-flavored gelatin

4 clear plastic cups

Gummy fish

HOW TO MAKE IT

❶ Fill each cup with blueberry-flavored gelatin.

❷ Gently place 1-2 gummy fish into each cup.

❸ Top with whipping cream and serve.

PROJECT TIPS & IDEAS

✓ Fill a clear plastic party bag with blueberry-flavored gelatin, place an orange gummy fish in the center of the gelatin and tie the bag shut with a ribbon. This project looks just like the gold fish in a bag many of us have won at a carnival or fair.

✓ Make a large Edible Ocean by filling a new fish bowl full of blueberry-flavored gelatin and gummy fish. You can even use grapes for gravel and shoestring licorice for seaweed.

Chocolate Spoons

Chocolate Spoons are great for eating ice cream and stirring hot cocoa.

WHAT YOU WILL NEED

1 cup milk chocolate chips

12 plastic spoons

Wax paper

HOW TO MAKE IT

❶ Pour chocolate chips into a microwaveable bowl and place in the microwave for 5 minutes on the medium setting. Remove from microwave and stir.

❷ Keep repeating the above process until the chocolate chips are melted.

❸ Dip the end of the plastic spoons into the melted chocolate and place them on a sheet of wax paper to harden.

PROJECT TIPS & IDEAS

✓ Try rolling your Chocolate Spoons in nuts and sprinkles before they harden.

✓ Turn your Chocolate Spoons into tasty gifts by wrapping the chocolate-covered end of the spoon in plastic wrap and tying it with a ribbon.

Fruity Leather Roll-Ups

Everyone will enjoy making our updated version of this delicious classic treat.

WHAT YOU WILL NEED

2 cups applesauce

1/4 cup honey

Microwaveble plastic wrap

Microwaveble tray

HOW TO MAKE IT

❶ Stir applesauce and honey together in a small bowl.

❷ Line a microwaveble tray with plastic wrap.

❸ Pour a 1/8-inch layer of the applesauce/honey mixture on top of the plastic wrap.

❹ Dry the mixture in the microwave on the medium setting for 3 minutes. Let the mixture cool for 3 minutes and then repeat the process until the fruity leather begins to dry. Results may vary, depending on the wattage of the microwave.

❺ Remove the fruity leather from the tray, keeping the plastic wrap as backing. Cut the leather into strips and roll them up.

PROJECT TIPS & IDEAS

✓ For added flavor, sprinkle the applesauce honey mixture with cinnamon before placing it in the microwave.

Bird Cookies

Our feathered friends chirp over these tasty cookie treats, which are for the birds.

WHAT YOU WILL NEED

1 cup softened unsalted butter

3 beaten eggs

1 tsp. baking soda

Mixed birdseed

3-1/2 cups flour

Pinch of salt

HOW TO MAKE IT

❶ Stir flour, baking soda and salt together in a large bowl.

❷ Add butter and eggs. Mix until well blended.

❸ Roll dough out on a floured surface and cut different shapes with cookie cutters.

❹ Make a hole in the top of each cookie with a drinking straw.

❺ Press birdseed into each side of the cookies.

❻ Bake at 350 degrees for 10-12 minutes.

❼ When Bird Cookies are cool, tie a ribbon or string through the hole and hang them on a tree limb.

PROJECT TIPS & IDEAS

✓ Make another great bird treat by covering a pine cone with peanut butter and rolling it in birdseed. Tie a string around the pine cone and hang it outside on a tree branch.

Kooky Cookie Paint

With this wacky-and-wild concoction, young Picassos can actually eat their works of art.

WHAT YOU WILL NEED

Need Adult!

1 beaten egg yolk

4-6 drops food coloring

Store-bought sugar cookie dough

Wax paper

Paintbrushes

HOW TO MAKE IT

❶ Mix the egg yolk and food coloring in a small bowl. Repeat this process several times to create different colors of Kooky Cookie Paint.

❷ Roll out the cookie dough on wax paper and cut out assorted shapes and sizes with cookie cutters.

❸ Place the cookies on a greased cookie sheet.

❹ Using Kooky Cookie Paint and paintbrushes create different designs and pictures on your cookies.

❺ Bake as directed on the package of cookie dough.

PROJECT TIPS & IDEAS

✓ Before baking sprinkle cookies with colored sugar or candy sprinkles.

Candy Jewelry

Create brightly colored necklaces and bracelets you can wear and eat.

WHAT YOU WILL NEED

Shoestring licorice

Cereal with holes in the middle

Hard candy with holes in the middle

HOW TO MAKE IT

❶ Cut a piece of shoestring licorice to the desired length. Make the pieces longer for a necklace or shorter for a bracelet.

❷ String cereal and hard candy onto the shoe string licorice creating different designs and patterns.

❸ Tie the loose ends of the licorice around your neck or wrist.

PROJECT TIPS & IDEAS

✓ Candy jewelry makes great birthday favors or a wonderful activity for a slumber party.

Shake & Make Whipped Cream

Use a peanut butter jar and a few kitchen ingredients to create tasty whipped cream in minutes.

WHAT YOU WILL NEED

1 large plastic peanut butter jar

1 pint heavy whipping cream

1 tsp. vanilla extract

1 tbs. powdered sugar

HOW TO MAKE IT

❶ Pour heavy whipping cream, powdered sugar and vanilla extract into a plastic peanut butter jar.

❷ Screw the lid on the peanut butter jar as tight as possible.

❸ Shake the jar in an up-and-down motion for 5-10 minutes or until the mixture turns into a thick, fluffy cream.

PROJECT TIPS & IDEAS

✓ Create different flavors of Shake & Make Whipped Cream by adding 1 tsp. of chocolate syrup, maple syrup or flavored extract.

✓ Add a drop of food coloring to the mixture before shaking to create whipped cream in an assortment of bright colors.

Chocolate Clay

With this concoction you can sculpt and eat your incredible clay creations.

WHAT YOU WILL NEED

Need Adult!

10 oz. semisweet chocolate chips

1/3 cup light corn syrup

HOW TO MAKE IT

❶ Pour chocolate chips into a microwaveable bowl and place in the microwave on high for 1 minute.

❷ Stir the chocolate and place back in the microwave for 1 minute or until the chocolate is melted.

❸ Stir in the corn syrup.

❹ Spread out the chocolate 1/2-inch thick on a sheet of wax paper.

❺ Let the chocolate set overnight. It will stiffen and become pliable. Now you are ready to sculpt.

PROJECT TIPS & IDEAS

✓ Make Chocolate Clay in a wide variety of colors by using white chocolate chips and stirring in a few drops of food coloring before the corn syrup is added.

Funny Face Toast

With this concoction you can create funny faces, pictures and designs that will brighten up your morning toast.

WHAT YOU WILL NEED

2 tbs. milk

2 drops food coloring

Paintbrush

Slice of bread

HOW TO MAKE IT

❶ Mix milk and food coloring in a small dish.

❷ Use a paintbrush to paint a face or design on the slice of bread.

❸ Toast the bread in a toaster set on the light setting.

PROJECT TIPS & IDEAS

✓ Funny Face Toast is great when used to make peanut butter and jelly or BLT sandwiches.

✓ Use Funny Face Toast to kick off a holiday breakfast. Paint a heart on your toast for Valentine's Day, a shamrock for St. Patrick's Day, a pumpkin for Halloween, etc.

Movie Glass Candy

It's just like the breakable glass used in the movies, only you can eat it!

WHAT YOU WILL NEED

2 cups sugar

1 cup water

Shallow, disposable aluminum pan

HOW TO MAKE IT

❶ Mix sugar and water together in a small saucepan.

❷ With the help of an adult, stir the mixture over medium heat until the sugar is dissolved and the mixture is completely clear.

❸ Remove the saucepan from the stove and let the liquid cool.

❹ Pour the mixture into a shallow disposable aluminum pan.

❺ Within 7-10 days, the liquid will turn into a sheet of sugar glass.

❻ Drain the remaining liquid from the pan. Carefully remove the sugar glass from the pan and place it on several layers of paper towels.

❼ Break the Movie Glass Candy with a small hammer and enjoy a tasty candy treat.

PROJECT TIPS & IDEAS

✓ Make Stained Movie Glass Candy by stirring a few drops of food coloring into the candy mixture.

✓ Remember our Movie Glass Candy is really candy. Real glass is dangerous and should never be eaten under any circumstances.

Peppermint Wreaths

Peppermint wreaths are a great alternative to hanging candy canes on the Christmas tree.

WHAT YOU WILL NEED

Bag of peppermint disks

Small aluminum pie tins

Cookie sheet

Ribbon

HOW TO MAKE IT

❶ Arrange peppermint disks in pie tins, in the shape of a circle, making sure the disks are touching each other. Place on cookie sheet.

❷ Place the cookie sheet in a preheated oven at 250 degrees for 3-5 minutes or until the peppermint disks melt together. Remove the cookie sheet from the oven and let the Peppermint Wreaths cool for 15 minutes.

❸ Use a spatula to carefully remove the cooled Peppermint Wreaths from the pie tins.

❹ Use ribbon to tie a bow around the top of the Peppermint Wreaths.

PROJECT TIPS & IDEAS

✓ Use different types of hard candy and your imagination to create wreaths and other original designs.

Soda Pop Potion

Our fizzing soda pop concoction will tickle your taste buds and astonish your friends.

WHAT YOU WILL NEED

4 tbs. lemon juice

2 tsp. baking soda

2 tbs. confectioners' sugar

2 quarts cold water

4-6 drops food coloring

HOW TO MAKE IT

❶ Stir water, food coloring, confectioners' sugar and baking soda together in a pitcher until blended.

❷ Stir in the lemon juice and your concoction should begin to fizz.

PROJECT TIPS & IDEAS

✓ Create multicolored ice cubes for your Soda Pop Potion by adding a few drops of food coloring to some water before freezing it in an ice cube tray.

✓ Make some color-change magic by adding blue ice cubes to a yellow Soda Pop Potion. As the ice cubes melt, the soda will turn green!

Frosting Dough

This edible dough is a fantastic way to top off any birthday cake or cupcake.

WHAT YOU WILL NEED

1 can frosting

1-1/2 cups powdered sugar

1 cup peanut butter

6-8 drops food coloring

HOW TO MAKE IT

❶ Mix frosting, powdered sugar, food coloring and peanut butter together in a large bowl.

❷ Knead the mixture until it turns into a dough.

❸ Mold with Frosting Dough as you would any other dough.

PROJECT TIPS & IDEAS

✓ Use Frosting Dough to create animals, people, flowers and other unique works of edible art.

✓ Frosting Dough sculptures can be used to garnish desserts such as cake, pies and ice cream.

Pickle Potion

With this clever concoction you can transform cucumbers into pickles in just a few hours.

WHAT YOU WILL NEED

1 large washed cucumber

1 tbs. sugar

2 tbs. salt

1 cup cider vinegar

Fork

WHAT YOU WILL NEED

❶ Use the prongs of a fork to make deep lengthwise grooves in the skin of the cucumber.

❷ Have an adult slice the cucumber as thin as possible. Paper-thin slices work best.

❸ Pour salt into a bowl. Toss the cucumber slices around in the bowl until they are completely covered with salt.

❹ Place an airtight cover on top of the bowl. Let the mixture sit for 1 hour at room temperature.

❺ Drain any liquid from the bowl.

❻ Mix the sugar and vinegar and pour it over the cucumbers.

❼ Chill the cucumbers in the refrigerator for 3-4 hours and then serve.

PROJECT TIPS & IDEAS

✓ Try garnishing the pickles with dill before serving.

✓ Use the pickles on your favorite sandwich or eat them as a snack.

Gooey Gumdrops

These tasty treats are sure to please even the most discriminating sweet tooth.

WHAT YOU WILL NEED

4 tbs. unflavored gelatin mix

1 cup cold water

1 cup heated fruit juice

3-4 drops peppermint extract

Food coloring

2 cups sugar

WHAT YOU WILL NEED

❶ Mix gelatin, water, extract and food coloring together in a small bowl. Let the mixture stand for 5 minutes.

❷ Add the heated fruit juice to the gelatin mixture. Stir until the gelatin is dissolved.

❸ Pour the mixture into a small shallow baking pan.

❹ Place the pan into the refrigerator overnight.

❺ Cut the Gooey Gumdrops into small squares and then roll them in sugar.

PROJECT TIPS & IDEAS

✓ Experiment by using different flavors of extract to make your Gooey Gumdrops.

✓ Match the flavor of extract used with the color of food coloring (yellow for lemon, red for peppermint, etc.).

✓ Ask an adult to help you heat the fruit juice.

Gelatin Oranges

These tasty treats look just like real orange wedges and make the perfect low-fat snack.

WHAT YOU WILL NEED

Oranges

1 box orange-flavored gelatin

WHAT YOU WILL NEED

❶ Have an adult cut the oranges in half and scoop out the center, leaving the outer skin.

❷ Prepare the box of gelatin by following the printed instructions on the package.

❸ Instead of pouring the liquid gelatin into a bowl to gel, pour it into the orange halves.

❹ Place the orange halves full of gelatin into the refrigerator to gel for 8 hours.

❺ Remove the orange halves from the refrigerator and have an adult cut the oranges into wedges.

PROJECT TIPS & IDEAS

✓ Use different types of citrus fruit (grapefruit, lemons and limes) along with different flavors of gelatin to create unique tasty treats.

✓ Follow the directions on the package of gelatin, except try substituting orange juice in place of the water, to create Gelatin Oranges bursting with flavor.

Tasty Taffy

This concoction captures the taste of old-fashioned taffy.

WHAT YOU WILL NEED

Need Adult!

1 cup sugar

1/4 cup water

2 tbs. vinegar

1 tbs. butter

1/2 tsp. vanilla

HOW TO MAKE IT

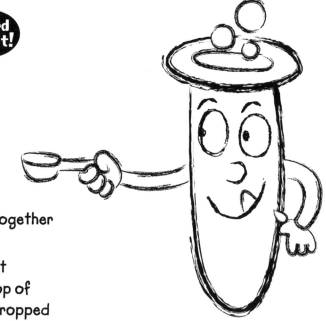

❶ Mix the sugar, water and vinegar together in a large pot.

❷ Have an adult boil the mixture until it reaches the "hardball stage" (a drop of the mixture turns into a ball when dropped in cold water.)

❸ Stir in butter and vanilla and then pour the mixture into a shallow pan that's coated with butter.

❹ Let the mixture cool for 1 hour.

❺ Butter your hands and then twist, pull and fold the mixture until it becomes a creamy color and difficult to pull.

❻ Roll the taffy into a long rope, cut it into small pieces and wrap the pieces in wax paper.

PROJECT TIPS & IDEAS

✓ Try adding a few drops of food coloring to the sugar, water and vinegar mixture to make different colors for your taffy.

✓ Put a handful of homemade Tasty Taffy into a glass jar and give it as a gift.

Kooky Concoctions

Fantasy Fossils

These make-believe fossils look and feel as if they're real.

WHAT YOU WILL NEED

2 cups quick-setting plaster of Paris

1 cup water

Sand

HOW TO MAKE IT

❶ Fill a pan or bowl with sand. Sprinkle the sand lightly with water until it is moist enough to hold an impression.

❷ Make an impression in the sand using hard objects such as a shell, a rubber lizard or even your own hand.

❸ Mix water and quick-setting plaster of Paris in a small bowl.

❹ Immediately pour the plaster mixture into the sand impression. Be careful not to let the plaster touch the edge of the pan, or the fossil will be difficult to remove.

❺ Let the plaster dry for 35-45 minutes or until hardened.

❻ Remove fossil from sand.

PROJECT TIPS & IDEAS

✓ Create color-tinted Fantasy Fossils by mixing in 1 tbs. of powdered tempera paint to the plaster before adding water.

83

Invisible Ink

With this easy ink recipe you can write secret messages that are visible only when exposed to heat.

WHAT YOU WILL NEED

2 tbs. pure lemon juice

Cotton swab

HOW TO MAKE IT

❶ Pour lemon juice into a small glass or plastic dish.

❷ Soak one end of the cotton swab in the lemon juice.

❸ Use the lemon juice-soaked cotton swab to write a secret message or draw a picture on a sheet of paper.

❹ When you are ready to view your secret message, have an adult hold the sheet of paper near a light bulb or over a toaster. The heat source will slowly turn the lemon juice dark brown and reveal the message.

PROJECT TIPS & IDEAS

✓ Create a secret treasure map using Invisible Ink.

✓ Write top-secret notes and messages that only your friends can read.

Fruity Lip Gloss

You can make this tasty lip gloss at home using nothing more than common kitchen ingredients.

WHAT YOU WILL NEED

2 tbs. solid shortening

1 tbs. fruit-flavored powdered drink mix

Plastic vitamin bottle or clean yogurt container

HOW TO MAKE IT

❶ Mix shortening and drink mix in a small microwaveable bowl until smooth.

❷ Place bowl in the microwave on high for 30 seconds until mixture becomes a liquid.

❸ Pour the mixture into a small, clean airtight plastic container.

❹ Place the Fruity Lip Gloss mixture in the refrigerator for 20-30 minutes or until firm.

PROJECT TIPS & IDEAS

✓ Decorate your Fruity Lip Gloss container using markers, glitter or adhesive-backed shelf paper.

✓ Create a Fruity Lip gloss necklace by placing an O-ring (found in any hardware store) around a plastic container filled with Fruity Lip Gloss. Tie a piece of yarn or string to the O-ring.

World's Best Bubbles

After testing dozens of bubble recipes, we found this one to be the best of the best.

WHAT YOU WILL NEED

2-1/2 qts. water

1/2 cup light corn syrup

1 cup liquid dish detergent

HOW TO MAKE IT

❶ Mix water and corn syrup together until completely blended.

❷ Gently stir in the liquid dish detergent.

❸ World's Best Bubbles will store for several weeks in an airtight container.

PROJECT TIPS & IDEAS

✓ Add a little color to your bubbles by stirring in a few drops of food coloring.

✓ Create bubbles in many different sizes by dipping various items such as a plastic strawberry basket or wire whisk into the bubble solution.

Walk of Fame Stones

Use Walk of Fame Stones to bring a touch of Hollywood to your backyard or garden.

WHAT YOU WILL NEED

Old bucket

8 cups quick-setting cement

Water

Shallow cardboard box (11-inch x 16-inch works best)

Stick or wooden spoon

Ruler

HOW TO MAKE IT

❶ Mix cement and 2 cups of water in a bucket until the mixture is the consistency of oatmeal. Add more cement or water if necessary.

❷ Pour the mixture evenly into the cardboard box. Your cement should be at least 1-1/2 to 2 inches thick.

❸ Take an old ruler and rake across the top of the cement until smooth. Wait 5 minutes.

❹ Place your hands or feet into the wet cement and push down 1-2 inches to make your impression. Immediately rinse your hands/feet with water.

❺ Use a stick or pencil to write your name, age or date in the cement.

❻ Let the cement dry 48 hours. Tear away the cardboard box and place your Walk of Fame Stone in your backyard or garden.

PROJECT TIPS & IDEAS

✓ Personalize your Walk of Fame Stone by adding seashells, toy cars, marbles, coins, dominoes, old jewelry, etc.

Crystal Rock Garden

Grow beautiful multicolored crystals using just a few simple household ingredients.

WHAT YOU WILL NEED

1 small sponge	4 tbs. salt
2 tbs. water	2 tbs. liquid bluing
Food coloring	Rubber glove

HOW TO MAKE IT

❶ Cut a sponge into several small pieces. Place sponge pieces in a small plastic or glass bowl.

❷ Put on rubber gloves, sprinkle 2 tbs. salt, water and liquid bluing over the sponge pieces. Allow it to set for 24 hours.

❸ Sprinkle the remaining 2 tbs. of salt over the sponge pieces. Allow the concoction to set for an additional 24 hours.

❹ Repeat step 2. Then add a few drops of food coloring to each sponge piece. By this time your Crystal Rock Garden should be starting to bloom.

PROJECT TIPS & IDEAS

✓ You can use cotton balls, coal or porous brick pieces in place of a sponge to create your Crystal Rock Garden.

✓ Crystal Rock Garden is a great science experiment that demonstrates how crystals form and grow.

Grass Head Guy

You'll be amazed to watch these cute little guys grow hair that you can cut and style.

WHAT YOU WILL NEED

Nylon stocking	6 tbs. potting soil
2 tbs. grass seed	Plastic yogurt container
2 google eyes	Glue
Water	Waterproof markers

HOW TO MAKE IT

❶ Cut a 4-inch-long piece of nylon stocking including the toe. Spoon grass seed into the stocking.

❷ Pour potting soil into the stocking until you have a ball of soil that is about 2 inches in diameter.

❸ Tie a knot in the stocking so that the soil will hold its ball shape. (Do not cut the tail off the stocking.)

❹ Glue a set of google eyes on your Grass Head Guy and then draw a nose and mouth using waterproof markers.

❺ Pour 1 to 2 inches of water into the bottom of the yogurt container.

❻ Place your Grass Head Guy in the yogurt container making sure the nylon tail sits in the water.

❼ Check the water in the plastic yogurt container daily.

PROJECT TIPS & IDEAS

✓ You can decorate the plastic yogurt container to look like a body using markers, glue and construction paper.

Silly Stained Glass

With this amazing concoction you can create the look of real stained glass.

WHAT YOU WILL NEED

Colored tissue paper

Liquid starch

Paintbrush

HOW TO MAKE IT

❶ Cut colored tissue paper into different shapes and sizes.

❷ Paint the liquid starch on a clear plastic or glass surface.

❸ Place the tissue paper pieces on top of the starch-covered item while smoothing out any wrinkles and covering all blank spaces.

❹ Silly Stained Glass will dry in 4-6 hours.

PROJECT TIPS & IDEAS

✓ Create a sparkling candle by covering the outside of a baby food jar with Silly Stained Glass and then placing a small votive candle inside the jar.

✓ After your Silly Stained Glass has dried, you can create the look of lead by outlining the tissue paper pieces with a black felt-tip marker.

Fruity Tie-Dye Shirts

Create cool temporary tie-dye T-shirts using nothing more than fruit flavored drink mix.

WHAT YOU WILL NEED

1 package of unsweetened drink mix (2 tbs.)

1/4 cup white vinegar

2 cups cold water

Rubber bands

T-shirt

Rubber gloves

HOW TO MAKE IT

❶ Mix drink mix, vinegar and water together in a small pot.

❷ Bring the mixture to a boil over medium heat.

❸ Remove the mixture from heat and let it cool.

❹ Scrunch the T-shirt up into a ball and wrap several rubber bands around it.

❺ Put on rubber gloves and dip the T-shirt in the Fruity Tie-Dye solution several times.

❻ Allow the T-shirt to set overnight until dry then remove the rubber bands to reveal your Fruity Tie-Dye Shirt.

PROJECT TIPS & IDEAS

✓ Use Fruity Tie-Dye to color Easter eggs.

✓ Make several different colors of Fruity Tie-Dye to create multicolored shirts.

Wacky Space Balls

These wild and Wacky Space Balls make great ornaments and look cool when hung from the ceiling.

WHAT YOU WILL NEED

1/3 cup quick-setting plaster of Paris

3 tbs. water

1 tbs. powder or liquid tempera paint

String or yarn

Balloon

HOW TO MAKE IT

❶ Blow up the balloon.

❷ Mix plaster of Paris, water and paint together in a small bowl.

❸ Soak string or yarn in the plaster mixture.

❹ Squeeze excess plaster off the string or yarn and wrap it around the balloon. Then, sprinkle it with glitter.

❺ Let the plaster dry for 2 hours and then pop the balloon with a pin.

❻ Tie a string around the Wacky Space Ball and hang it as an ornament or from the ceiling.

PROJECT TIPS & IDEAS

✓ Try adding liquid tempera paint to the plaster before dipping the yarn or string.

✓ Jazz up your Wacky Space Ball by painting it with liquid tempera paint.

✗ Remember to pick up all of the balloon pieces and throw them in the trash.

Cool Crayon T-Shirts

Create some of the coolest T-shirts you have ever seen with nothing more than a box of crayons.

WHAT YOU WILL NEED

Box of crayons

100% cotton T-shirt

Wax paper

Iron

HOW TO MAKE IT

❶ Using the box of crayons create and color a picture or design on your cotton T-shirt.

❷ Put the shirt on an ironing board.

❸ Place a sheet of wax paper over the picture or design.

❹ Place an iron on the cotton setting and have an adult iron the back of the wax paper for 15-30 seconds. This will make your design permanent.

PROJECT TIPS & IDEAS

✓ Try making some Cool Crayon napkins, aprons and place mats. Always make sure you only use 100% cotton fabric.

✓ Cool Crayon T-Shirts are great for creating custom shirts for school clubs, scouts or your next family reunion.

Kooky Clingers

Create your very own Kooky Clingers to stick on windows or jars.

WHAT YOU WILL NEED

1/4 cup white glue

7-10 drops food coloring

Plastic overhead sheet or sheet protector

Paintbrush

HOW TO MAKE IT

❶ Mix white glue and food coloring in a small bowl.

❷ Brush a thick layer of the glue and food coloring mixture onto the plastic sheet to create a design. Do not leave any blank spots or white spaces in your design.

❸ Let the design set 24 hours or until dry.

❹ Peel the design off the plastic sheet and stick it to any glass surface.

PROJECT TIPS & IDEAS

✓ Draw a picture on a sheet of paper, then lay the plastic sheet on top of the paper. Trace the design with the food coloring-and-glue mixture to create foolproof stickers every time.

✓ Add a little bit of glitter to the glue mixture to make your Kooky Clingers sparkle.

Filter Flowers

Create a brightly colored bouquet of tie-dye flowers using only a few household ingredients.

WHAT YOU WILL NEED

3 coffee filters

10-12 drops food coloring

1/4 cup water

Green pipe cleaner

HOW TO MAKE IT

❶ Mix water and food coloring in a small dish. Repeat this step 2-3 times using different colors of food coloring.

❷ Fold each of the 3 coffee filters into fourths.

❸ Dip each edge and corner of the filters in a different color of the food coloring/water mixture.

❹ Unfold the filters and set them on a paper towel until they are dry.

❺ Place the 3 filters on top of each other.

❻ Grab the middle or bottom point of the filters and wrap with the top 3 inches of the green pipe cleaner. Pull the rest of the pipe cleaner straight down to form a stem.

PROJECT TIPS & IDEAS

✓ Make a Filter Butterfly by clipping the middle of two colored coffee filters with a clothespin. Glue on google eyes and small pieces of black pipe cleaners for antennae.

Crystal Sculpting

Create 3-D crystal sculptures that make dazzling tree ornaments and package ties.

WHAT YOU WILL NEED

Need Adult!

Large jar
Borax laundry booster
Pencil
Water

Pipe cleaners
String
Food coloring

HOW TO MAKE IT

❶ Have an adult fill the jar with boiling water.

❷ Pour borax into the jar one spoonful at a time until it no longer dissolves and settles on the bottom of the jar.

❸ Stir in 10-12 drops of food coloring.

❹ Bend a pipe cleaner into different shapes, sizes and forms.

❺ Tie one end of the string around the pipe cleaner sculpture and the other around a pencil.

❻ Place the pencil on the jar opening so the pipe cleaner is suspended in the middle of the borax solution.

❼ Let the solution stand overnight. Remove the crystal-covered sculpture and let it dry.

PROJECT TIPS & IDEAS

✓ Tie several different Crystal Sculptures together to create a mobile for your bedroom.

Magic Photo Art

Transform black and white photos from newspapers or magazines into wacky works of art.

WHAT YOU WILL NEED

Black and white picture from a magazine or newspaper

Colored pencils, markers, crayons or watercolor paints

HOW TO MAKE IT

❶ Cut a black and white picture from a magazine or newspaper.

❷ Give the picture new life by coloring it in with colored pencils, markers, crayons or watercolor paints.

PROJECT TIPS & IDEAS

✓ Take a picture of your family, friends or pet and copy it on a black and white photocopier, then color it in.

✓ Try creating your own greeting cards with your magic photos.

Spaghetti Art

Turn cold leftover spaghetti into the hottest works of 3-D art you've ever seen.

WHAT YOU WILL NEED

White school glue

Cold cooked spaghetti

Wax paper

Assorted colors of glitter

HOW TO MAKE IT

❶ Pour some school glue into a small bowl.

❷ Dip a few strands of spaghetti at a time into the white school glue.

❸ Create different designs by arranging the glue-covered spaghetti strands on a sheet of wax paper. Make sure all the strands of spaghetti are connected and touching each other.

❹ Sprinkle the glue-covered spaghetti with glitter.

❺ Let your design set overnight or until dry.

❻ Carefully peel the wax paper away from the Spaghetti Art.

PROJECT TIPS & IDEAS

✓ Use Spaghetti Art and some string to create awesome mobiles, ornaments and package ties.

✓ Create cool winter window decorations by creating spaghetti snowflakes and sprinkling them with silver glitter.

Crayon Melt Art

You'll be amazed as you watch old crayons melt together to create stained glass-like designs.

WHAT YOU WILL NEED

Old crayons

Wax paper

Kitchen grater

Iron

HOW TO MAKE IT

❶ Have an adult grate up the old crayons and separate them by color.

❷ Use a felt-tip pen to draw a bold design on a sheet of wax paper.

❸ Fill the design with the grated bits of crayons.

❹ Carefully place another sheet of wax paper on top of your crayon-filled drawing.

❺ Have an adult iron the top of the wax paper with an iron on the low setting. Continue ironing until the crayon wax melts together.

PROJECT TIPS & IDEAS

✓ Use Crayon Melt Art to create sparkling sun catchers and other stained glass-like window decorations.

Super Bubble Ooze

This amazing concoction can stretch, bounce and blow up like a balloon.

WHAT YOU WILL NEED

1/4 cup liquid laundry starch

1/4 cup school glue gel

1 drop food coloring

HOW TO MAKE IT

❶ Pour school glue gel into a small bowl. Add 1 drop of food coloring and stir until blended.

❷ Slowly pour the glue and food coloring mixture into a bowl containing 1/4 cup of liquid starch.

❸ Let the mixture sit for five minutes. Remove it from the bowl and then slowly knead it with your hands until the glue absorbs almost all of the liquid starch. The more you knead your Super Bubble Ooze, the firmer it will become.

❹ Store Super Bubble Ooze in a ziplock bag or airtight container.

PROJECT TIPS & IDEAS

✓ Place a blob of Super Bubble Ooze on the end of a straw and blow it up like a balloon.

✓ Roll Super Bubble Ooze into a ball and see how high it will bounce.

Phony Spill

This Phony Spill looks so real that even your mom won't know it's really fake.

WHAT YOU WILL NEED

1/2 cup white school glue

1 tbs. poster paint or tempera paint

Paper cup

Wax paper

HOW TO MAKE IT

❶ Mix glue and paint in a small bowl.

❷ Pour the mixture into a paper cup.

❸ Lay the paper cup on its side on top of a large sheet of wax paper. This will form the Phony Spill.

❹ Let the Phony Spill dry on the wax paper 1-2 days, or until completely dried.

❺ Slowly peel the dry Phony Spill and cup from the wax paper.

❻ Phony Spill is most effective when placed on a floor or countertop. Never place Phony Spill on fabric or on a carpet.

PROJECT TIPS & IDEAS

✓ Use a chocolate syrup can, mustard bottle or ketchup bottle in place of the paper cup.

✓ Try placing a drinking straw or other objects in the Phony Spill to make it even more realistic.

Magic Egg Writing

With this concoction any message you write on the outside of an eggshell will disappear and then reappear inside the egg.

WHAT YOU WILL NEED

1 cup white vinegar

1 Tbs. alum (found in the spice section of most grocery stores.)

Egg

Fine-tip paintbrush

HOW TO MAKE IT

❶ Mix white vinegar and alum together in a small bowl.

❷ Dip the brush into the mixture and write a message on the eggshell.

❸ Let the shell dry completely and then have an adult boil the egg for 15 minutes.

❹ Let the boiled egg cool.

❺ Peel off the eggshell and the message will appear inside the egg.

   ***DO NOT EAT THE EGG.

PROJECT TIPS & IDEAS

✓ Put on a magic show for your friends. Pass the egg around and let everyone examine it. They will be amazed when you peel off the shell to reveal a message or their name.

Silly Scents

Use this concoction to create your own custom brand of perfume or cologne.

WHAT YOU WILL NEED

2 tbs. rubbing alcohol

1 tbs. grated lemon peel
(You can also use one or more of the following: grated orange peel, cloves, rose petals, vanilla bean or mint leaves.)

1 plastic container with snap-on lid
(like a vitamin or yogurt container, wash before using)

HOW TO MAKE IT

❶ Place grated lemon peel in the plastic container.

❷ Pour rubbing alcohol on top of the lemon peel.

❸ Place the lid on top of the plastic container and shake.

❹ Let the mixture set for several days, shaking it at least once a day.

❺ The perfume/cologne is ready to wear when it smells like the scent you created and not like alcohol.

PROJECT TIPS & IDEAS

✓ Create a custom label for your Silly Scents using markers or stickers.

✓ Pour your Silly Scents mixture into a small fancy bottle, tie a ribbon around it and give as a gift.

Magic Movie Blood

Make fake blood just like the kind used in many Hollywood movies.

WHAT YOU WILL NEED

1 cup light corn syrup

10 drops red food coloring

1 drop blue food coloring

1 tbs. water

HOW TO MAKE IT

❶ Mix corn syrup and water in a small bowl until well blended.

❷ Add red and blue food coloring to the mixture and stir until blended.

PROJECT TIPS & IDEAS

✓ Make alien blood by using green food coloring instead of red and blue.

Plastic Gelatin

With this concoction you can create homemade plastic that looks like stained glass.

WHAT YOU WILL NEED

1 envelope unflavored gelatin

4 drops food coloring

3 tbs. hot water

Disposable pie tin

HOW TO MAKE IT

❶ Mix unflavored gelatin and hot water in a small bowl until the gelatin is completely dissolved.

❷ Add food coloring and stir until blended.

❸ Pour the mixture into a disposable pie tin.

❹ Let the mixture dry for 2-3 days or until the edges are hard.

❺ Peel the Plastic Gelatin from the pie tin and cut it into a shape using scissors.

PROJECT TIPS & IDEAS

✓ Use Plastic Gelatin to create a mobile, sun catcher, guitar pick or bookmark.

✓ Try adding a little bit of glitter to the Plastic Gelatin mixture before it dries.

Liquid Layer Art

It's just like sand art only you use different types of colorful liquids instead of sand!

WHAT YOU WILL NEED

2-3 drops red food coloring

2-3 drops blue food coloring

1/4 cup water

1/4 cup cooking oil

1/4 cup rubbing alcohol

Tall clear drinking glass

HOW TO MAKE IT

❶ Mix red food coloring and water in a small bowl. Pour the liquid into a tall glass.

❷ Slowly pour oil into the glass on top of the water.

❸ Mix blue food coloring and rubbing alcohol in a small bowl. Slowly pour the liquid into the glass on top of the oil.

PROJECT TIPS & IDEAS

✓ Try creating your Liquid Art in fancy bowls or bottles to create a real conversation piece.

✓ Experiment by using other types of liquids colored with food coloring such as corn syrup.

Wacky Tattoos

Make your own washable tattoos!

WHAT YOU WILL NEED

Paper towels

Washable markers

Water

HOW TO MAKE IT

❶ Cut or tear the paper towel into small squares.

❷ Use the washable markers to draw pictures and designs on the small squares of paper towels to make your Wacky Tattoos.

❸ Wet the back of your hand, and place your tattoo face-down on your hand.

❹ Using the palm of your other hand, firmly push on the back of the tattoo to transfer it onto your skin.

❺ Wacky Tattoos can be removed easily with soap and water.

PROJECT TIPS & IDEAS

✓ Celebrate your favorite holiday by making holiday-themed Wacky Tattoos to give to your friends and family members.

✓ Have a Wacky Tattoo party. Make and trade tattoos with your friends.

Goofy Gel Air Freshener

Make your own great smelling gel air freshener just like the ones sold in stores.

WHAT YOU WILL NEED

2 envelopes unflavored gelatin (2 tbs.)

15 - 20 drops perfume, cologne or other fragrance

1/2 cup hot water

1/2 cup ice-cold water

Food coloring

Baby food jar

HOW TO MAKE IT

❶ Mix gelatin and hot water in a bowl until the gelatin is completely dissolved.

❷ Stir in food coloring and fragrance.

❸ Add ice-cold water and stir.

❹ Pour the mixture in a baby food jar and let it set overnight at room temperature or until it turns into a gel.

PROJECT TIPS & IDEAS

✓ Do not place Goofy Gel Air Freshener in the refrigerator or the smell will be absorbed by your food.

✓ Decorate the baby food jars with ribbon, stickers or wrapping paper and give as a gift.

Handprints in the Sand

Capture your handprint and the feeling of being at the beach with this fun, easy-to-create concoction.

WHAT YOU WILL NEED

Need Adult!

Plaster of Paris

Water

Sand

Box

HOW TO MAKE IT

❶ Fill your box with moist hard-packed sand.

❷ Push both hands down into the sand to create an impression at least 1/2-inch to 2 inches deep.

❸ Mix plaster of Paris according to the directions on the package and then pour the mixture into the handprints.

❹ Let the mixture set for 45 minutes and then remove the handprints from the sand.

❺ Let the handprints dry in a sunny window for 1 hour.

PROJECT TIPS & IDEAS

✓ Make a hanger for your handprints by pushing a paper clip into the plaster of Paris before it is completely dry.

✓ Use your feet to make footprints in the sand instead of handprints.

Crystal Farm

Grow real crystals in this amazing underwater garden.

WHAT YOU WILL NEED

Small clear glass bowl

Assorted rocks, pebbles and seashells

2 ounces alum (found in the spice section of most grocery stores)

1/2 cup hot water

HOW TO MAKE IT

❶ Fill the clear glass bowl half full with rocks, pebbles, or seashells.

❷ Mix water and alum until alum is completely dissolved.

❸ Pour the mixture over the contents of the bowl.

❹ Within a few hours, crystals should begin to grow. After several days you should have many large crystals growing in your Crystal Farm.

PROJECT TIPS & IDEAS

✓ Try adding a few drops of food coloring to the water and alum mixture to grow colored crystals.

Disappearing Eggshell

Turn ordinary hard-boiled eggs into rubber eggs using this simple science concoction.

WHAT YOU WILL NEED

1 hard-boiled egg

1 jar with lid

White vinegar

HOW TO MAKE IT

❶ Place the hard-boiled egg into the jar.

❷ Fill the jar with white vinegar.

❸ Screw on the lid and let the egg sit for 3 days.

❹ After 3 days the eggshell will be gone leaving a thin white membrane. The egg will look and feel like rubber.

PROJECT TIPS & IDEAS

✓ This concoction is a great science experiment, demonstrating the chemical reaction calcium carbonate (the eggshell) and vinegar have when mixed together.

Sandpaper Transfer Art

With Sandpaper Transfer Art you can make copies of your favorite crayon drawings to share with family and friends.

WHAT YOU WILL NEED

Sandpaper

Crayons

White paper

HOW TO MAKE IT

❶ Push down hard on your crayons and draw a picture on a piece of sandpaper.

❷ Place the sandpaper, drawing side down, onto a sheet of plain white paper.

❸ Have an adult iron the back of the sandpaper with an iron set on low.

❹ Carefully peel the sandpaper off of the white paper to reveal a copy of your drawing.

PROJECT TIPS & IDEAS

✓ Use Sandpaper Transfer Art to create unique holiday cards and stationery.

✓ Try creating a picture with a white crayon and then transfer it to a black sheet of paper.

Cherry-Scented Volcano

This amazing concoction begins with a fizz and then erupts in a bubbling flow of cherry-scented lava.

WHAT YOU WILL NEED

1/4 cup baking soda

8-oz plastic bottle

1/4 cup flour

1 tbs. cherry- flavored powder drink mix

5 cups water

Newspaper (torn into strips)

1/4 cup vinegar

1 cup cold water

24-inch cardboard square

Need Adult!

HOW TO MAKE IT

❶ Mix flour and 1 cup of water in a small bowl until smooth.

❷ Heat 5 cups of water in a large saucepan over medium heat until the water begins to boil.

❸ Add flour-and-water mixture to the boiling water. Continue to boil while constantly stirring for 3-5 minutes.

❹ Remove pan from heat and allow paste mixture to cool.

❺ Secure the plastic bottle in the center of your cardboard square. Dip newspaper strips in the paste mixture. Cover the bottle and cardboard with layers of the paste-coated newspaper strips until it looks like a volcano. Be sure not to cover the opening of the bottle.

❻ Let the volcano set for 24 hours or until completely dry. Now you can paint and decorate your volcano. Allow the volcano to dry.

❼ Now you are ready to make your volcano erupt. Pour baking soda and drink mix into the bottle. Add the vinegar and the colorful scented eruption will begin.

PROJECT TIPS & IDEAS

✓ Try creating a pretend island around the base of your volcano, using paint, small twigs and dried grass.

Holiday Concoctions

New Year's!

New Year's is a time to celebrate the passing of one year and the beginning of another. Although many cultures observe this holiday at different times, the start of a new year is always a cause for celebration.

Tips for a great New Year's celebration

Make it a tradition to spend this time as a family. If you go out on New Year's Eve, then schedule your family time on New Year's Day. Family games or a night at the movies is a great way to begin your evening celebration.

Have everyone write down their goals and dreams for the New Year and hide them in a secret place until next year's celebration. It's fun to see how many came true.

Look through family photos together from the past year.

Bang on pots and pans outside and cheer with excitement at midnight.

New Year's Noisemakers

This homemade Noisemaker is a perfect way to bring in the New Year.

WHAT YOU WILL NEED:

2 clear plastic cups

1/4 cup mixed dried beans, rice and macaroni

Colored tape

HOW TO MAKE IT

❶ Pour dried beans, rice and macaroni into one clear plastic cup.

❷ Place the other plastic cup on top of the first cup so that they are rim to rim.

❸ Securely tape the two cups together and shake.

PROJECT TIPS & IDEAS

✓ Decorate the outside of your New Year's Noisemakers with markers or construction paper.

✓ Jazz up your shakers by adding a little bit of glitter or confetti.

99

Party Wands

Use Party Wands to bring in the New Year with an explosion of glitter and confetti.

WHAT YOU WILL NEED

Paper towel tube

Confetti

Construction paper or markers

Clear tape

HOW TO MAKE IT

❶ Cover one end of the paper towel tube with tape.

❷ Decorate the tube with New Year's Eve designs using markers, construction paper and clear tape.

❸ Fill the tube with confetti.

❹ Wad up a piece of paper and place it in the open end of the tube to keep the glitter and confetti in place.

❺ Just before midnight, remove the wad of paper. When the clock strikes midnight, wave the Party Wands in the air to create an explosion of confetti.

PROJECT TIPS & IDEAS

✓ Add glitter and thin streamers to your Party Wands.

✓ Fill your Party Wands with treats and pieces of candy.

Confetti Balloons

This New Year's Eve party favor will explode into a cloud of confetti.

WHAT YOU WILL NEED

1 large balloon

1/4 cup paper confetti

Toothpick

Funnel

HOW TO MAKE IT

❶ Pull the balloon over the end of the funnel.

❷ Pour confetti into the balloon.

❸ Remove the balloon from the funnel and blow it up, being careful not to get any confetti in your mouth.

❹ Tie the balloon shut.

❺ When the clock hits midnight, yell, "Happy New Year". Hold the Confetti Balloon away from your face and pop it with a toothpick.

PROJECT TIPS & IDEAS

✓ Write a New Year's message on a piece of paper, roll it up and place it in the balloon before blowing it up.

✓ Use felt-tip markers to decorate the outside of your Confetti Balloons.

✗ Remember to pick up all balloon pieces and throw them in the trash. Especially if there are small children in the house!

Valentine's Day!

Valentine's Day is the day each year set aside to celebrate the love we have for our friends, family and sweethearts. It is often celebrated with the exchange of fancy cards, flowers and candy.

Tips for a special Valentine's Day

Make a special Valentine's Day flower bouquet. Get white carnations and place them in a mixture of red food coloring and water. It is fun to watch the magical transformation as the white flowers suddenly become tipped in red.

Serve a meal with red napkins and heart-shaped white lace doilies that you can find at your supermarket. Place a homemade heart place card at everyone's seat and have a candlelight dinner.

Have each family member make a valentine for another family member telling one thing that they really like about that person. This can be fun with friends, too.

Sweetheart Chocolate Roses

These Sweetheart Chocolate Roses are not only beautiful to look at, they're also good to eat!

WHAT YOU WILL NEED

Bag of small chocolate kisses

Red or pink plastic wrap

Green tape   Clear tape

Green pipe cleaners   Green tissue paper

HOW TO MAKE IT

❶ Make your rosebud by taping two foil wrapped kisses together end to end with plastic tape.

❷ Cut and drape a 5-inch square of plastic wrap over the point of the top kiss and gather the edges, twisting them into a tail at the point of the bottom kiss.

❸ Twist the top of a green pipe cleaner around the tail to form a stem.

❹ Add leaves by twisting the pipe cleaner once around the center of a green strip of tissue paper.

❺ Cut each end of the tissue paper strip so that the tissue paper resembles rose leaves. Repeat the above steps several times to make a bouquet of Sweetheart Chocolate Roses.

PROJECT TIPS & IDEAS

✓ Arrange several Sweetheart Chocolate Roses in a vase with real greens and give it as a Valentine's Day gift.

✓ Use different colors of plastic wrap to create a bouquet of roses in assorted colors.

101

Cookie Bouquet

Instead of giving your loved one a bouquet of flowers, why not try giving this fun-to-make Cookie Bouquet?

WHAT YOU WILL NEED

Need Adult!

1 package (18 ounces) refrigerated chocolate chip cookie dough

8 flat wooden sticks

HOW TO MAKE IT

❶ Preheat oven to 375 degrees.

❷ Roll the dough into eight 2-inch balls. Place the balls on an ungreased cookie sheet.

❸ Insert the wooden sticks into each ball so that they look like a lollipop. Slightly flatten the dough.

❹ Bake 13 to 15 minutes or until the edges of the cookies are crisp.

❺ Ask an adult to help take the cookies out of the oven and to help transfer the cookies to a wire rack. Allow them to cool completely.

❻ Put your cookies together to form a bouquet and give as a gift.

PROJECT TIPS & IDEAS

✓ Jazz up your Cookie Bouquet by tying a red ribbon around each stick and then wrap the cookie in colored plastic wrap.

✓ Arrange your Cookie Bouquet in a small glass vase or floral box, just like you would a bouquet of flowers.

Giant Chocolate Kiss

Make a Giant Chocolate Kiss, just like the ones you buy in the store. It's bound to put a smile on anyone's face.

WHAT YOU WILL NEED

Need Adult!

1 bag of milk chocolate chips

Round funnel   Coffee mug

Nonstick spray   Foil

HOW TO MAKE IT

❶ Melt the chocolate chips in the microwave or in a double boiler.

❷ Place some aluminum foil over the small end of a funnel.

❸ Place the funnel upright in a coffee mug. Spray the funnel with nonstick cooking spray.

❹ Pour the melted chocolate into the funnel and place it in the freezer for 45 minutes or until the chocolate has hardened completely.

❺ Remove the chocolate from the funnel and wrap it in tin foil.

❻ Write a message on a narrow piece of paper. Tuck the end of it into the aluminum foil at the point of the kiss.

PROJECT TIPS & IDEAS

✓ This project can also be made using white chocolate chips and peanut butter chips.

✓ Try wrapping red plastic wrap over the foil for an even more festive look.

St. Patrick's Day!

This holiday pays tribute to St. Patrick, the patron saint of Ireland, and was originally celebrated by people of Irish descent. Shamrocks and the color green are the most common symbols of St. Patrick's Day.

Tips for a fun St. Patrick's Day

Draw a little shamrock on the back of your hand or on your cheek with a washable non-toxic marker.

Dress in green from head to toe.

For a fun drink, add a few drops of green food coloring to your milk. You can also add green food coloring to other foods such as scrambled eggs, cake icing, mashed potatoes, pancakes, or anything else you can think of.

Shamrock Glass Cookies

Celebrate St. Patrick's Day with these cookies, which look like stained glass and taste like candy.

WHAT YOU WILL NEED

Need Adult!

1 package of premade sugar cookie dough

Green hard candy (Lifesavers® or Jolly Ranchers®)

Ziplock bags

Rolling pin

2 shamrock-shaped cookie cutters (1 large, 1 small)

HOW TO MAKE IT

❶ Roll out cookie dough and cut out cookies using the large shamrock cookie cutter. Using the small shamrock cookie cutter cut a hole in the center of each cookie.

❷ Place cookies on a foil-covered cookie sheet.

❸ Put hard candies in a ziplock bag and crush them using the rolling pin.

❹ Use the crushed candy to fill the holes in the center of the cookies.

❺ Have an adult help you bake your cookies at 375 degrees for 8-10 minutes or until lightly brown. Cool completely and then peel the cookies off the foil.

PROJECT TIPS & IDEAS

✓ Make this project using other holiday-shaped cookie cutters and colored candies (e.g. heart-shaped cookie cutters and red candy for Valentine's Day).

103

Leprechaun's Lucky Shake

Children and leprechauns of all ages will enjoy this minty ice-cold shake.

WHAT YOU WILL NEED

1 cup milk

1 scoop vanilla ice cream

2 ice cubes

3-4 drops mint extract to taste

2 drops green food coloring

HOW TO MAKE IT

❶ Place milk, ice cream and ice cubes in a blender and blend on high for 10 seconds.

❷ Add mint extract and 2 drops of green food coloring and blend for an additional 10 seconds.

❸ Pour Leprechaun's Lucky Shake into a glass and serve.

PROJECT TIPS & IDEAS

✓ Spice up your shake by adding a little whipped cream and a cherry on top.

✓ Give your shake a little zing by adding a splash of seltzer water.

Emerald Isle Shamrock

This living shamrock will delight adults and amaze children as it grows.

WHAT YOU WILL NEED

Potting soil

Quick-growing grass seed

Pencil

Pie tin

Plant mister

HOW TO MAKE IT

❶ Fill a pie tin with a 3-inch layer of potting soil.

❷ Spray a light layer of water over the soil with a plant mister.

❸ Use a pencil to draw a picture of a shamrock in the moist soil.

❹ Sprinkle a thin layer of grass seed inside of your shamrock and cover with a 1/4-inch layer of soil. Mist with water.

❺ Place your Emerald Isle Shamrock in a sunny window and mist with water 1-2 times a day. The seeds will begin to sprout in just a few days.

PROJECT TIPS & IDEAS

✓ Try using other types of seeds such as herb seeds.

✓ Draw a picture of a Christmas tree in the soil and grow a living tree during the Christmas season.

Easter

Easter is a holiday that celebrates the rebirth of Christ. It is also a time to celebrate the coming of Spring. Bunnies, colored eggs, baby chicks and lilies are often used as symbols of this holiday.

Tips for a Happy Easter

Use the Kid Concoctions® Treasure Stones dough recipe found on page 129 to cover your treat-filled plastic eggs. It will make your Easter egg hunt much more challenging and fun.

Have a family egg hunt with plastic eggs filled with coupons from Mom or Dad that spell out special rewards or privileges. Some of our family favorites are: "You don't have to make your bed today." "You can stay up one half-hour past bedtime." "Mom will clean your room today." "I owe you one dollar."

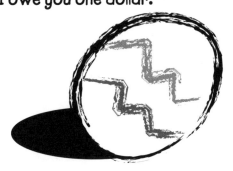

Mystery Message Eggs

Family and friends will have fun breaking open real eggs with hidden messages inside.

WHAT YOU WILL NEED

Eggs	Toothpick or pin
Paper	Colored markers
Turkey baster	

HOW TO MAKE IT

❶ Use a toothpick or pin to poke a small hole in one end of an egg and a large hole in the other end.

❷ Use a turkey baster to suck out the contents of the egg through the large hole.

❸ Carefully rinse the eggshell out with soap and water. Shake excess water out of the eggshell and allow it to dry.

❹ Carefully decorate your eggshells with colored markers or with the Quick & Easy Egg Dye recipe on page 106.

❺ Write messages on small pieces of paper, then roll up the message and place it in the egg through the large hole.

PROJECT TIPS & IDEAS

✓ Paint designs on your Mystery Message Eggs using a mixture of 3-4 drops of food coloring to 1 tbs. water.

✓ Put dollar bills in your Mystery Message Eggs and hide them in the backyard for the ultimate egg hunt.

Living Basket

Celebrate this holiday of rebirth by growing your very own basket of Easter grass.

WHAT YOU WILL NEED

Colored plastic wrap

Grass seed (wheat seed or rye seed)

Potting soil

Basket

Plant mister

HOW TO MAKE IT

❶ Line the basket with plastic wrap leaving a 1-inch lip hanging over the side of the basket.

❷ Fill the basket with 3-4 inches of soil.

❸ Sprinkle a fine layer of grass seed over the soil and then cover the grass seed with 1/4-inch of potting soil. Spray with plant mister.

❹ Place the basket in a warm, sunny window and spray the soil with a plant mister 2-3 times a day. After 4-5 days, your grass will begin to sprout. You should have a beautiful basket of grass in 2-3 weeks.

PROJECT TIPS & IDEAS

✓ Plant some flower seeds in your Living Basket and give it to a friend or family member as a gift.

✓ Decorate your basket with ribbon and fill it with beautiful Easter eggs to make the perfect Easter dinner centerpiece.

Quick & Easy Egg Dye

This concoction lets you create beautiful colored eggs in minutes.

WHAT YOU WILL NEED

1 tbs. food coloring

1 tbs. vinegar

Hard-boiled eggs

Water

HOW TO MAKE IT

❶ Combine food coloring and vinegar in a small bowl until blended.

❷ Add enough water to make the liquid deep enough to cover an egg.

❸ Swirl the liquid around with a spoon. Quickly lower an egg into the solution and remove.

❹ Pat the egg dry with a paper towel.

❺ Put a little bit of cooking oil on a paper towel and rub the egg with it. This will give the egg a varnished look.

PROJECT TIPS & IDEAS

✓ Draw a design on your egg with a white crayon before dipping. The dye will not stick to your design.

✓ Make different colors of egg dye. Dip one half of the egg in one color and the other half in another color.

Cinco de Mayo!

This is a festival of Mexican heritage that is celebrated with mariachi music, folkloric dancing and Mexican food.

Tips for a super Cinco de Mayo celebration

Decorate your kitchen and prepare a Mexican meal.

Learn Spanish words by making special flash cards.

Wear a "sombrero" (Mexican hat) and a "serape" (shawl worn over one shoulder), even if you have to make your own out of things you have around the house.

Play some Mexican music or sing Mexican songs and have a "fiesta".

Cinco de Mayo Corn Chips

Children will be amazed that they can make these delicious corn chips at home.

WHAT YOU WILL NEED

Need Adult!

1/2 cup yellow cornmeal

1/2 tsp. salt

1 cup very hot water

3/4 cup very hot water

1 tsp. margarine

HOW TO MAKE IT

❶ Mix cornmeal and salt in a large bowl.

❷ Pour in one cup of hot water and margarine, and stir until margarine is melted.

❸ Add 3/4 cup of hot water and stir.

❹ Drop spoonfuls of the corn chip mixture onto a greased cookie sheet.

❺ Bake at 450 degrees for 12-15 minutes or until golden brown. Get an adult to help you with the oven.

PROJECT TIPS & IDEAS

✓ Add a few drops of food coloring to your Cinco de Mayo Corn Chips to make a colorful and tasty bowl of chips.

Quick & Easy Salsa

This classic homemade salsa tastes great and is very easy to make.

WHAT YOU WILL NEED

2-3 medium tomatoes, chopped

1/2 cup chopped onion

1-2 serrano chilies or jalapenos, seeds removed

1/3 cup chopped cilantro

1 tsp. salt

Juice from 1/4 fresh lime

HOW TO MAKE IT

❶ Mix all of the ingredients together in a small bowl.

❷ Cover the mixture and let it sit for one hour before serving.

PROJECT TIPS & IDEAS

✓ Serve Quick & Easy Salsa with Cinco de Mayo Corn Chips for a tasty snack.

✕ Only adults should handle the chilies. Be sure to wash hands immediately after handling.

108

Party Piñata

This classic concoction recipe has been a favorite of children for many years.

WHAT YOU WILL NEED

1 cup cold water

1/4 cup flour

5 cups water

Large inflated balloon

Long, narrow newspaper strips

HOW TO MAKE IT

❶ Mix flour and 1 cup of water in a small bowl until smooth.

❷ Heat 5 cups of water in a large saucepan over medium heat until the water begins to boil.

❸ Add flour /water mixture to boiling water. Continue to boil, while stirring constantly for 3-5 minutes. Get adult help for steps 2 and 3.

❹ Remove pan from heat and allow papier-mâché paste to cool.

❺ Dip strips of newspaper in papier-mâché paste and place them over the blown-up balloon, leaving a small hole at the top. This hole needs to be just big enough to accommodate candy and small gifts. Place several layers of papier-mâché newspaper strips over the balloon so that your piñata is sturdy.

❻ After the newspaper strips have dried, pop the balloon and fill the empty cavity with candy and toy prizes. Seal the hole with duct tape and decorate the piñata with paint, colored markers, streamers and crepe paper.

PROJECT TIPS & IDEAS

✓ Suspend the piñata and take turns with your friends trying to hit it with a stick while blindfolded. Eventually, the piñata will break open, releasing the candy and toy prizes.

✓ Party Piñatas are also great for birthday parties and other celebrations.

Mother's Day

Mother's Day is a holiday celebrated in the United States on the second Sunday in May. On Mother's Day children show their love and appreciation for their mothers by honoring them with gifts, flowers and cards.

Tips to make Mother's Day even more special

Give Mom a fresh bouquet of flowers. The flowers that children pick for their mothers in their own yard are just as special as the ones bought in the store.

Write Mom a love letter. She will probably keep it for a very long time.

Make coupons for Mom that say the things you will do to help her around the house. Moms can always use a cheerful helper.

Start Mom's special day by serving her juice, coffee or even breakfast in bed.

Beauty Bath Salts

Mom will love taking a nice, relaxing bath in Beauty Bath Salts that you can make yourself.

WHAT YOU WILL NEED

1 clear plastic peanut butter jar (wash out and remove label)

2 cups Epsom salt

1 cup coarse salt

Food coloring

Perfume or essential oil (for fragrance)

HOW TO MAKE IT

❶ Mix both kinds of salt together in a bowl. Add 2-3 drops of food coloring and mix.

❷ Add 5-6 drops of perfume or essential oil and stir.

❸ Spoon the mixture into jar and screw on the lid.

❹ Make a gift tag with the name of the fragrance used and include directions that suggest using 1/3 to 1/2 cup of Beauty Bath Salts in the bathtub.

PROJECT TIPS & IDEAS

✓ Make and layer different colors of salt in the plastic jar to create a sand art effect.

✓ Decorate the top of your jar by placing a small square of fabric over it and then secure the fabric with a rubber band.

Petal Potpourri

Mom will love this mixture of beautiful flower petals which will make any room smell good.

WHAT YOU WILL NEED

2 cups flower petals (rose petals work best)

1/4 cup whole cloves

2 tbs. salt

Small basket or bowl

HOW TO MAKE IT

❶ Put the petals in a large bowl.

❷ Sprinkle salt and cloves over the petals and gently stir.

❸ Place the mixture in a small basket or bowl and give as a gift along with an instruction card that states "Stir once a day to keep your room smelling nice." (After a few days the petals will begin to dry, but they will look and smell fresh for months.)

PROJECT TIPS & IDEAS

✓ Add some small pine cones and a couple of cinnamon sticks to your potpourri to make it smell and look even nicer.

✓ After the flower petals are completely dry the potpourri can be stored in ziplock bags or in an airtight container.

Quilted Pot

Mothers will love this beautiful, easy-to-make pot which looks like a quilt.

WHAT YOU WILL NEED

Scrap pieces of fabric cut into 2-3 inch squares

White glue

Terra-cotta pot

Paintbrush

HOW TO MAKE IT

❶ Paint a thin layer of white glue on the back of a fabric square and then stick it to the outside of the pot.

❷ Repeat the above step several times until the entire outside of the pot is covered with fabric squares.

❸ Let the pot dry overnight.

PROJECT TIPS & IDEAS

✓ Plant a flower or plant in your pot, and tie a ribbon around it before giving as a gift.

✓ To make the outside of the pot waterproof, apply several layers of clear spray shellac.

Father's Day

Father's Day became an official United States holiday in 1972. It was created to celebrate fathers and express thanks to them for the important roles they have played in their children's lives.

Tips for making Father's Day special

Make your Dad a special card telling him all the things you really like about him.

Make some coupons for Dad telling him you'll help with some of his chores. Some good ideas could be: "I will help you wash the car." "I will take out the trash today." "I will help you work in the yard."

Pet Rock Paperweight

Dad will love it when you give him your own version of a 1970's fad that took the country by storm.

WHAT YOU WILL NEED

Clean rounded rock
Paint or colored markers
Google eyes
White glue

HOW TO MAKE IT

❶ Draw or paint a mouth, nose and ears on your rock.

❷ Use the white glue to apply the google eyes to your pet rock.

❸ Let the rock dry overnight.

PROJECT TIPS & IDEAS

✓ Use paper and colored markers to create a birth certificate for your pet rock. Be sure to include a name and birthdate.

✓ Be creative and use other materials such as feathers, sequins and buttons to decorate your Pet Rock Paperweight.

Mosaic Masterpieces

A great Father's Day gift! You'll be amazed how quick and easy it is to create these beautiful Mosaic Masterpieces.

WHAT YOU WILL NEED

Plaster of Paris

Water

Assorted beads, buttons, marbles, stones, coins or mosaic tiles

Small, shallow plastic dish

HOW TO MAKE IT

❶ Mix plaster of Paris and water following the directions on the plaster of Paris package.

❷ Pour the plaster mixture into a small, shallow plastic dish, filling it half full. Let the plaster dry for a few minutes until it feels like a soft clay. Be careful not to let the plaster dry too long.

❸ Quickly push the assorted beads, buttons, marbles, stones, coins or mosaic tiles into the plaster to make pictures and designs.

❹ Let your mosaic dry overnight before trying to remove it from the dish.

PROJECT TIPS & IDEAS

✓ Create a coaster by making your mosaic in a small, round plastic dish. Glue a piece of felt on the bottom of the coaster to prevent it from scratching furniture.

Puzzle Frames

This is a unique and unusual Father's Day gift that will be cherished for years to come.

WHAT YOU WILL NEED

Picture frame (flat frames work best)

White glue

Old puzzle pieces

Poster paint

Paintbrush

HOW TO MAKE IT

❶ Paint old puzzle pieces various colors using a paintbrush and poster paint. Make sure you have enough painted puzzle pieces to cover the front of your frame.

❷ After the puzzle pieces have completely dried, lay the frame flat and use white glue to attach the puzzle pieces to the frame. Let the frame dry overnight.

❸ Put a favorite picture of you and Dad in the frame and give it as a Father's Day gift.

PROJECT TIPS & IDEAS

✓ Experiment by creating different types of frames decorated with other household objects such as buttons, coins, etc.

Independence Day

Independence Day is a U.S. holiday celebrated on July 4th of each year to mark the American colonies' freedom from England. Many other countries around the world celebrate their own Independence Day.

Tips for making your Independence Day even more fun

Have a family barbeque or picnic. Serve red, white and blue foods on colored plates.

Wear red, white and blue clothing. Attend a parade in your community or watch the fireworks with family.

Take along snacks and blankets to make it more festive.

Firecracker Paint Pens

They look like Independence Day firecrackers, but they are actually roll-on paint pens.

WHAT YOU WILL NEED

Need Adult!

Empty roll-on deodorant bottles

Liquid tempera paint or washable poster paint

Yellow, orange and red construction paper

Tape or glue

String or yarn

HOW TO MAKE IT

❶ Have an adult use a screwdriver to pop the roll-on ball out of the deodorant bottle.

❷ Rinse out the bottle and fill it with liquid tempera paint or poster paint.

❸ Snap the roll-on ball back into the bottle.

❹ Use the construction paper and tape or glue to decorate the deodorant bottle. Make it look like a firecracker and make the cap look like a flame.

PROJECT TIPS & IDEAS

✓ Add fine glitter to your Firecracker Paint Pen to create glitter paint.

✓ Decorate the paint pens to look like snowmen and use them to celebrate winter holidays.

Tie-Dye Flowers

These red, white and blue Tie-Dye Flowers will amaze your friends and family.

WHAT YOU WILL NEED

Long-stemmed white carnation

Red and blue food coloring

Two 8 oz. glasses filled with water

Green thread

HOW TO MAKE IT

❶ Squeeze 7-8 drops of red food coloring in one glass of water and 7-8 drops of blue food coloring in the other glass of water.

❷ Have an adult use a sharp knife to cut the stem of the carnation lengthwise, making it into two thin stems.

❸ Set the two glasses together. Place one half of the carnation stem in the red water and the other half in the blue water.

❹ After several hours, the carnation should begin to turn red, blue and white. The longer the flower stays in the solution, the brighter the color will be.

❺ Remove the carnation from the food coloring solutions and wrap the stems together with green thread. Place the carnation in a clear vase of water.

PROJECT TIPS & IDEAS

✓ Make several different Tie-Dyed Flowers to create an entire bouquet.

✓ Make different colored flowers for other holidays.

Party Crackers

Party Crackers make great favors for Independence Day picnics and are sure to be a hit with children of all ages.

WHAT YOU WILL NEED

Toilet paper tubes

Tissue paper

Colored markers, stickers or poster paint

Ribbon

Tape

Candy, coins, marbles, small toys, etc.

HOW TO MAKE IT

❶ Tape one end of the toilet paper tube closed. Fill the tube with candy, coins, marbles, small toys or anything else that will fit. Tape shut the other end of the tube.

❷ Wrap the tube with tissue paper and then tie the ends with ribbon. Construction paper or gift wrap can also be used.

❸ Decorate the outside of the tube with markers, stickers or poster paint.

❹ When you finish your picnic, distribute your Party Crackers. People should pull hard on both ends of their Party Crackers to open them.

PROJECT TIPS & IDEAS

✓ Party Crackers also make great favors for birthday parties, Christmas, Hanukkah, Kwanzaa or Halloween.

Grandparent's Day

This holiday was created to honor and give thanks to our grandparents for all they have done to enrich our lives.

Tips for making Grandparent's Day special

Giving your grandparents a current photograph is always a welcome treat.

Create a photo scrapbook of you with your grandparents throughout the year.

Make a scrapbook of artwork and poetry you have created.

Make a special gift with all the grandchildren's handprints. You can use fabric paint to press all the hand prints on a tablecloth, shirt or smooth watercolor paper. Or use a fabric marker to outline all the hands on a sweatshirt. Be sure to add the names with a fabric marker. This will be a keepsake forever.

Glitter Candles

Your grandparents will be amazed by these one-of-a-kind Glitter Candles.

WHAT YOU WILL NEED

Pillar candle

White glue

Paintbrush

Glitter or sequins

HOW TO MAKE IT

❶ Paint the sides of the pillar candle with a thin layer of white glue.

❷ Sprinkle the sides of the candle with glitter or sequins until completely covered.

❸ Let the candle dry overnight before handling it.

PROJECT TIPS & IDEAS

✓ Glitter Candles can be made for any holiday or occasion.

✓ Try decorating the sides of a candle with nontoxic paint and colored markers.

Sparkle Votives

Grandma and Grandpa will love these sparkling votives made from just a few household items.

WHAT YOU WILL NEED

Glass baby food jar (washed with label removed)

White glue

Paintbrush

Salt

Small picture or stickers

HOW TO MAKE IT

❶ Paint a thin layer of glue on the back of your picture and stick it on the outside of the baby food jar.

❷ Paint over the picture and the outside of the jar with a thin layer of school glue.

❸ Sprinkle a generous amount of salt over the wet glue on the outside of the jar.

❹ Let the jar dry overnight, then place a tea candle inside of the jar.

PROJECT TIPS & IDEAS

✓ Create Sparkle Votives for other holidays by cutting pictures out of holiday greeting cards and magazines.

Magic Flower Stationery

Transfer the image of real flowers onto paper and create beautiful stationery, envelopes and greeting cards.

WHAT YOU WILL NEED

Rubber mallet or hammer

Plastic wrap

Fresh flowers (pansies, impatiens and geraniums work best)

Paper

Envelopes

HOW TO MAKE IT

❶ Arrange flowers face-down on a sheet of paper in a border pattern.

❷ Carefully cover the flowers with a sheet of clear plastic wrap.

❸ Gently hit the flowers with the rubber mallet being careful not to miss any parts of the flower.

❹ Remove the plastic wrap and flowers from the paper to reveal your Magic Flower Stationery.

PROJECT TIPS & IDEAS

✓ Use the Magic Flower method to make custom greeting cards and invitations.

✓ Use the Magic Flower method to decorate paper napkins and place mats for your next picnic.

Halloween

Halloween is a celebration that reflects customs and superstitions that have been gathered through the ages. In the United States, children carve pumpkins and dress in masks, makeup and costumes to celebrate this holiday.

Tips for a fun and spooky Halloween

Plan a party with your friends and have everyone dress up in a costume. You may want to serve a fall treat such as hot apple cider, doughnuts or cookies.

Make little ghosts by tying a facial tissue around a lollipop. You can use a felt-tip marker to create eyes on your friendly ghost.

Decorate your house by making pumpkins, cats, bats or ghosts out of construction paper.

Swamp And Snake Dessert

This *yummy* treat is sure to give a ghoulish end to any Halloween meal.

WHAT YOU WILL NEED

1 cup premade vanilla pudding

3-4 drops green food coloring

Gummy snakes or worms

2 crushed vanilla wafers

HOW TO MAKE IT

❶ Mix pudding and food coloring in a small bowl until well blended.

❷ Spoon the pudding into a small dessert dish.

❸ Sprinkle the top of the pudding with the crushed vanilla wafers.

❹ Add gummy snakes or worms and serve.

PROJECT TIPS & IDEAS

✓ Use different colors of food coloring to create Swamp and Snake Desserts in a variety of creepy colors.

✓ Spice up your Swamp and Snake Dessert by sprinkling mini-marshmallows on top of the pudding.

Monster Hand Punch

This tasty punch will give your party guests a monster laugh.

WHAT YOU WILL NEED

6 cups water

1 quart unsweetened grape juice

1 (6-ounce) can of frozen lemonade concentrate

1 (6-ounce) can of frozen orange juice concentrate

2 clean plastic gloves

Green food coloring

HOW TO MAKE IT

❶ Mix water, grape juice, lemonade and orange juice together in a large bowl. Place the bowl of fruit punch in the refrigerator.

❷ Wash out plastic gloves and fill with water.

❸ Add 3-4 drops of food coloring to the water inside the glove.

❹ Tie a knot in the top of the glove to keep the water from leaking out. Place the glove in the freezer for 3 hours or until it is frozen solid.

❺ Untie the knot in the gloves and peel the glove away from your monster hands. Place your monster hands into the bowl of fruit punch and serve.

PROJECT TIPS & IDEAS

✓ Fill a plastic glove with candy, plastic spiders and party favors and then tie the end with orange ribbon to create a creepy treat for party guests or trick-or-treaters.

Ghoul And Goblin Makeup

Transform yourself into a ghoul, goblin or any other Halloween character with this wonderful face paint.

WHAT YOU WILL NEED

2 tbs. solid shortening

1 tbs. cornstarch

4-6 drops food coloring

Small make-up sponges

HOW TO MAKE IT

❶ Mix shortening and cornstarch in a small bowl until smooth.

❷ Add 4-6 drops of food coloring. Mix until the color is evenly blended.

❸ Apply makeup to the face using a small makeup sponge.

❹ Remove makeup with soap and water.

PROJECT TIPS & IDEAS

✓ Add 1/2 tsp. of glitter to the makeup to make it sparkle.

✓ Try applying the makeup to your arms and hands for an even more frightening look.

Thanksgiving

In the United States Thanksgiving is one of the oldest and most widespread celebrations. This American holiday commemorates a harvest celebration held by the Pilgrims of Plymouth colony in 1621. There are also Thanksgiving holidays celebrated every year in Canada, Japan, South Korea, the Philippines, Puerto Rico and the Virgin Islands.

Tips for making Thanksgiving a great holiday

Give each family member an equal amount of dried beans, dried seeds or pennies. Pass a cup around the dinner table. Each person then tells everyone one thing that they are thankful for on this Thanksgiving and puts one of their beans in the cup. Keep passing the cup around until everyone has placed all their beans in the cup. We do this each year in our family and it is one of our favorite traditions.

Decorate your house with handmade decorations from the season such as turkeys, pumpkins, pilgrim hats or corn.

Pumpkin Candleholders

Use small pumpkins to create beautiful candleholders for your Thanksgiving dinner.

WHAT YOU WILL NEED

Need Adult!

2 small pumpkins
Knife
2 taper candles

HOW TO MAKE IT

❶ Have an adult use a knife to cut a hole in the top center of a small pumpkin. Make sure the hole is slightly smaller than the diameter of the candle you are using.

❷ Push the candle into the center of the pumpkin. Make sure the candle is as straight as possible.

PROJECT TIPS & IDEAS

✓ Try using red, green or yellow apples instead of small pumpkins to create holiday candleholders.

✓ Create an even more festive look by decorating your Pumpkin Candleholders with colored markers or poster paint.

✓ Draw Jack-o'-Lantern faces on your pumpkins with colored markers or paint and use them as Halloween decorations.

Indian Corn Jewelry

Indian Corn Jewelry is easy to make and has the look of polished stone jewelry.

WHAT YOU WILL NEED

1/2 cup dried Indian corn kernels

Sewing needle

Thread

Small bowl

Water

HOW TO MAKE IT

❶ Pour corn kernels into a small bowl of water.

❷ Let the corn kernels soak overnight in the water or until soft.

❸ Thread the needle, tying a knot at the end of the thread.

❹ Have an adult push the needle through each soft kernel of corn until the necklace or bracelet is as long as you want it to be. Tie both ends of the thread together.

PROJECT TIPS & IDEAS

✓ Try using dried sunflower seeds and yellow corn kernels along with the Indian corn to create even more beautiful bracelets and necklaces.

Native American Napkin Rings

Use household items to create these wonderful napkin rings which look like a Native American's headband.

WHAT YOU WILL NEED

Paper towel tubes

Construction paper

White glue

Scissors

Colored markers

HOW TO MAKE IT

❶ Cut a 3/4-inch wide circle from the paper towel tube. This will serve as the base of your napkin ring.

❷ Use colored markers to draw a Native American design on your napkin ring so that it looks like a headband.

❸ Cut small feathers from construction paper and fringe each side with scissors so it looks like a feather.

❹ Put a drop of glue on the bottom of the feather and attach it to the inside of the napkin ring. After the glue is dry, roll up a napkin and slide your napkin ring over it.

PROJECT TIPS & IDEAS

✓ Make fancy Native American Napkin Rings by gluing scraps of fabric over the napkin ring and using real feathers.

Hanukkah

This Jewish holiday has been celebrated for thousands of years. During the eight-day festival of lights, oil lamps containing only enough oil for one night miraculously burned for eight nights.

Tips for making Hanukkah special

Have a traditional "latkes" meal which is potato pancakes served with applesauce. Eat jelly doughnuts for dessert.

Make little "gelt" bags of chocolate coins or money coins.

Plan special events as a family for each of the eight days of Hanukkah.

Hanukkah Pretzel Sticks

These tasty chocolate covered pretzel-sticks make the perfect Hanukkah snack.

WHAT YOU WILL NEED

1 cup white chocolate chips

Pretzel rods

Blue candy sprinkles

Microwaveble bowl

Wax paper

HOW TO MAKE IT

❶ Pour chocolate chips into a microwaveable bowl and place in the microwave for 3 minutes or until melted. Have an adult remove the chocolate from the microwave and stir.

❷ Use a spoon to drizzle the chocolate over half of the pretzel rod and then sprinkle with blue candy sprinkles.

❸ Set the pretzel rods on wax paper for 30 minutes or until the chocolate has hardened.

PROJECT TIPS & IDEAS

✓ Use different types of candy or crushed nuts to create pretzel sticks for other holidays and special occasions.

✓ Try making pretzel sticks using milk chocolate chips or peanut butter chips.

Hanukkah Art Rubbings

Using this age-old rubbing technique children can create beautiful Hanukkah art and designs.

WHAT YOU WILL NEED

White school glue

Cardboard

Paper

Crayons with the paper removed

Pencil

HOW TO MAKE IT

❶ Use a pencil to draw different Hanukkah symbols such as a Star of David, menorah or dreidel.

❷ Trace your design with a bottle of white school glue.

❸ Let the school glue dry until hard.

❹ Place a sheet of paper over the glue drawing and rub the paper with a crayon held in the horizontal position. The image of your glue drawing will appear on the paper.

PROJECT TIPS & IDEAS

✓ Use Hanukkah Art Rubbings to create cards, wrapping paper and pictures to celebrate this wonderful holiday.

✓ Create different looks by using assorted colors of crayons and paper.

✓ Use the same technique to create rubbings for lots of other holidays such as Christmas, Easter and Halloween.

Star of David Sugar Sculptures

Create sparkling sugar sculptures using a few easy-to-find kitchen ingredients.

WHAT YOU WILL NEED

1/2 cup sugar

1 tsp. glitter

1 tsp. water

Star of David cookie cutter

HOW TO MAKE IT

❶ Mix all of the ingredients together in a small bowl.

❷ Press the sugar mixture into a cookie cutter.

❸ Tap the cookie cutter gently onto a plate until the sugar sculptures pop out of the cookie cutter.

❹ Let the sugar sculptures dry overnight before handling.

PROJECT TIPS & IDEAS

✓ Glue a loop of yarn onto the back of your sculptures to create pretty package ties and ornaments.

✓ Add a few drops of food coloring to the sugar mixture to make sugar sculptures in an assortment of colors.

✓ Use the same techniques to create sugar sculptures for other holidays.

❄ Christmas

The word Christmas comes from the Old English term Cristes maesse, meaning "Christ's mass," first held on December 25th. Today Christmas is celebrated around the world with festive decorations and the custom of exchanging gifts.

Tips for a wonderful Christmas holiday

Decorate a gingerbread house or make Christmas cookies together as a family.

Play Christmas music and sing along as you decorate your Christmas tree and home for the holiday.

Go caroling in your neighborhood with family and friends.

Give homemade gifts or cards to friends and family.

Snow in a Bottle

Enjoy the magic of a winter wonderland during the Christmas season and year round with this classic snow-globe concoction.

WHAT YOU WILL NEED

1 medium-size baby food jar

White glitter

Glue gun

Small plastic figure or decorations

Cold water

HOW TO MAKE IT

❶ Wash your baby food jar and remove label.

❷ Using a glue gun, attach the plastic figure or decorations to the inside of the jar lid.

❸ Fill the jar a 1/2-inch from the top with cold water.

❹ Add glitter.

❺ Screw lid on the jar, turn it upside down and shake.

PROJECT TIPS & IDEAS

✓ Use ribbon, a garland or plastic greenery to decorate the base of your snow globe.

✓ Add 2 drops of food coloring to the water in the Snow in a Bottle to create a colorful winter sky.

Gumdrop Ornaments

These pretty Christmas tree ornaments not only look great, they also taste pretty good, too.

WHAT YOU WILL NEED

Small round foam ball

Toothpicks

Gumdrops

String

HOW TO MAKE IT

❶ Push 3 gumdrops onto a toothpick leaving one end of the toothpick exposed.

❷ Push the exposed end of the toothpick into a foam ball. Repeat the above steps several times until you have made enough gumdrop toothpicks to cover the entire ball.

❸ Tie a string around the Gumdrop Ornament and hang it on your Christmas tree.

PROJECT TIPS & IDEAS

✓ Make unique ornaments by arranging different color gumdrops in various patterns on the foam balls.

Christmas Pomander Ball

This old-fashioned holiday air freshener has always been one of our family favorites.

AT YOU WILL NEED

1 orange

1/4 cup cinnamon

Ribbon

Whole cloves

Ziplock bag

String

HOW TO MAKE IT

❶ Push the pointed end of the whole cloves into the orange one at a time until the entire orange is covered with cloves.

❷ Pour the cinnamon into the ziplock bag. Place the orange in the bag and shake. Remove the orange from the bag and tie a piece of ribbon around the orange.

❸ Tie a second piece of ribbon around the orange so that it crisscrosses the first ribbon at the bottom. Tie a knot at the top.

❹ Tie a piece of string around the knotted ribbons. This will serve as a hanger for your Christmas Pomander Ball.

❺ The orange will eventually shrink and become rock hard. You can enjoy your Christmas Pomander Ball for many years to come.

PROJECT TIPS & IDEAS

✓ You can create a beautiful pomander arrangement by making several pomanders, tying different colors of ribbon around each one, and arranging them in a clear glass bowl.

✓ Use your pomander as a Christmas tree ornament or wrap it in a piece of netting and give it as a gift.

Chocolate Fudge Cocoa

Made with three kinds of chocolate, this is a chocolate lover's dream come true.

WHAT YOU WILL NEED

1/2 gallon white milk

2/3 cup milk chocolate chips

6 tbs. cocoa powder

1/3 cup sugar

1 quart chocolate milk

HOW TO MAKE IT

❶ Mix 1 cup of white milk, chocolate chips, cocoa and sugar together in a large saucepan. Cook over low heat until the sugar dissolves.

❷ Add the rest of the white milk and all of the chocolate milk. Stir the mixture until it begins to steam. Do not let the cocoa boil!

❸ Pour into cups and serve. If cocoa is too hot, let it cool before drinking. Makes 12 servings.

PROJECT TIPS & IDEAS

✓ Top your Chocolate Fudge Cocoa with miniature marshmallows or fresh whipped cream.

✓ When visiting friends or family during the holidays, take them a thermos full of Chocolate Fudge Cocoa with a gift tag attached containing the recipe.

Mini-Lanterns

These unique lanterns will bring lots of holiday cheer to any Christmas celebration.

WHAT YOU WILL NEED

Soup can
(with paper label removed)

Hammer   Nail

Paper   Votive candle

HOW TO MAKE IT

❶ Fill the soup can with water and place in the freezer for 24 hours or until frozen solid.

❷ Cut a piece of paper the same height as the can and long enough to be wrapped around the can.

❸ Use a pencil to draw a simple holiday design on the paper (e.g. Christmas tree, snowman, snowflake, etc.).

❹ When the water is completely frozen, remove the can from the freezer and wrap the paper around the can, securing it with a piece of tape.

❺ Lay the can on a thick, folded towel, and ask an adult to help you use the hammer and nail to punch holes along the lines of your design.

❻ Place the can in warm water until the ice is melted. Have an adult place a votive candle in the can.

PROJECT TIPS & IDEAS

✓ Place Mini-Lanterns on each side of your front door or along a driveway or front walkway.

✓ Mini-Lanterns can also be made for other holidays such as Hanukkah and Halloween.

Kwanzaa

This is an African-American festival that's celebrated around the world by millions of people of African descent. This week-long holiday celebrates African family, community and culture. Kwanzaa takes place from December 26 to January 1. The name Kwanzaa comes from Swahili and means "first fruits of the harvest".

Tips for a great Kwanzaa celebration

Plan a Kwanzaa celebration feast in your family.

Decorate with the colors of Kwanzaa, which are red, green and black.

Create your own place mat, which is one of the 7 symbols of Kwanzaa. The 7 symbols of Kwanzaa are crops, a mat, a candlestick, 7 unity candles, ears of corn, gifts and a unity cup.

Sand Beads

Make bead necklaces and bracelets that are similar to the beautiful ones worn by African women.

WHAT YOU WILL NEED

1 cup sand

1/4 cup white glue

Toothpick

Yarn or string

HOW TO MAKE IT

❶ Mix sand and glue in a small plastic bowl.

❷ Knead the mixture until it is the consistency of a stiff dough. If the mixture is too moist, add more sand.

❸ Pinch off a small piece of dough and roll it into the size of bead you want. Use a toothpick to make a hole in the middle of the bead that's big enough for your yarn or string to pass through.

❹ Allow the beads to dry overnight or until hard.

❺ Cut a piece of yarn or string to the desired size of necklace or bracelet. String the beads and then tie together your yarn or string.

PROJECT TIPS & IDEAS

✓ Make different colored beads by adding 1 tbs. of poster paint or liquid tempera paint to the sand mixture before mixing.

✓ Kwanzaa Sand Beads can be decorated with paints and colored markers.

Harvest Rain Stick

Children will have fun mixing seeds, beans and rice to create the sounds of a tropical African rain shower.

WHAT YOU WILL NEED

Heavy cardboard mailing tube

2 plastic caps or duct tape to seal the tube

Nails

Hammer

Seeds, rice and dried beans

Adhesive-backed shelf paper, wrapping paper, fabric, paint or ribbon

HOW TO MAKE IT

❶ Have an adult hammer nails into the mailing tube 1/8-inch apart using the spiral seam of the cardboard tube as a guide.

❷ Add several handfuls of assorted rice, seeds and beans.

❸ Seal each end of the tube securely with plastic caps or duct tape.

❹ Decorate your Harvest Rain Stick with ribbon, paint, adhesive-backed shelf paper, wrapping paper or fabric.

PROJECT TIPS & IDEAS

✓ Use your Harvest Rain Stick as a musical instrument. Shake it and twist it to create a wide variety of sounds.

✓ Decorate your Harvest Rain Stick by gluing seeds and beans on it in various patterns.

Kwanzaa Kabobs

You'll love celebrating the holiday of "first fruits" with these tasty, nutritious and easy-to-make kabobs.

WHAT YOU WILL NEED

Bamboo skewers

Grapes (washed and removed from the stem)

Bananas (peeled and sliced)

Can of pineapple chunks (drained)

Can of mandarin oranges (drained)

HOW TO MAKE IT

❶ Sort each type of fruit into a different bowl.

❷ Create unique and colorful patterns by pushing pieces of fruit onto the skewers.

❸ Serve Kwanzaa Kabobs by themselves or with plain yogurt for dipping.

PROJECT TIPS & IDEAS

✓ Create an interesting centerpiece for the dinner table by pushing Kwanzaa Kabobs into a large honeydew melon or cantaloupe.

✓ Experiment by making Kwanzaa Kabobs with different types of fruit such as strawberries, blueberries, watermelon, etc.

Birthdays

Your birthday is the anniversary of the day you were born. Although no one knows for sure when birthday celebrations began, we do know that birthdays have been celebrated since the early 14th century.

Tips for a great birthday

Throw your own Kid Concoctions® birthday party. Make some of your favorite concoctions at the party.

Have your party guests make their own ice cream with the Kid Concoctions® Shake and Make Ice Cream recipe found on page 71.

Make your own goody bags or gifts to give as party favors.

Edible Birthday Card

Why give a regular paper birthday card when you can give this easy-to-make Edible Card?

WHAT YOU WILL NEED

Need Adult!

1 package premade sugar cookie dough

1 egg yolk, beaten

Cookie sheet

Food coloring

Small paintbrushes

HOW TO MAKE IT

❶ Mix the egg yolk and food coloring in a small bowl. Repeat this process several times to make different colors of paint.

❷ Roll out the cookie dough on a greased cookie sheet.

❸ Cut and shape the dough to the desired card size.

❹ Use the small paintbrushes and the egg yolk/food coloring mixture to write a message and to paint a design on the card.

❺ Ask an adult to help you bake as directed on the package of cookie dough.

PROJECT TIPS & IDEAS

✓ Add pizzazz to your Edible Birthday Card by sprinkling it with candy sprinkles or colored sugar before baking.

✓ Wrap your Edible Birthday Card with color plastic wrap and tie a ribbon around it.

Birthday Cake Cookies

These wonderful cookies are easy to make and they taste just like a birthday cake.

WHAT YOU WILL NEED

1 box cake mix

2 eggs

1/2 cup vegetable oil

Nuts and chocolate chips (optional)

HOW TO MAKE IT

❶ Mix oil, eggs and cake mix in a large bowl.

❷ Stir in chocolate chips and nuts.

❸ Drop tablespoon-sized mounds of batter onto a greased cookie sheet.

❹ Get an adult to help you bake the Birthday Cake Cookies in a preheated oven at 350 degrees for 10 minutes.

PROJECT TIPS & IDEAS

✓ Experiment by using different flavors of cake mix.

✓ Decorate your Birthday Cake Cookies with frosting and candy sprinkles.

Treasure Stones

These stones can be broken open to reveal hidden treasures and secret messages.

WHAT YOU WILL NEED

1 cup flour

1 cup dry used coffee grounds

1/2 cup salt

3/4 cup water

Small plastic toy treasures

HOW TO MAKE IT

❶ Knead all ingredients in a small bowl until a stiff dough is formed.

❷ If the dough is too wet, add more flour to make it stiffer. If the dough is too dry, add more water.

❸ Divide the dough into 3 equal-size balls.

❹ Make a hole in the center of the balls big enough to hide several small plastic toy treasures. Fill the holes with treasures.

❺ Pinch the holes shut to cover the treasures.

❻ Have an adult help you bake the Treasure Stones in the oven on a foil-covered sheet for 25 minutes at 150 degrees. (DO NOT EAT THE TREASURE STONES!)

PROJECT TIPS & IDEAS

✓ Add 1 Tbs. of powdered tempera paint to tint your Treasure Stones different colors or roll in glitter to make Glitter Stones.

✓ Use Treasure Stones for party favors or a scavenger hunt at your next party.

4 Bonus Concoctions!

Magic Art Board

Press with your finger to draw and redraw colorful pictures on a squishy black background. Easy to erase with just a wipe of the hand.

WHAT YOU WILL NEED

1 gallon-size ziplock bag

1/2 cup black poster paint or finger paint

Photo mat for an 8-inch by 10-inch picture

8 1/2-inch by 11-inch sheet of paper

Crayons/markers

White glue

HOW TO MAKE IT

❶ Pour 1/2 cup of black paint into a gallon-size ziplock bag.

❷ Squeeze all the air out of the bag and seal the bag.

❸ Create a colorful abstract design on the paper with light colored markers or crayons. Then place the ziplock bag on top.

❹ Mount the ziplock bag and paper between an inexpensive cardboard photo mat and glue shut.

PROJECT TIPS & IDEAS

✓ Redraw different colorful backgrounds with crayons and markers to change it up.

✓ Decorate the frame with stickers or collage with colored paper.

✓ Great to take on long car trips!

Rainbow Paint

Create a full rainbow with one stroke of your brush!

WHAT YOU WILL NEED

3-inch foam brush

Paper

Food coloring (red, yellow and blue)

Water

HOW TO MAKE IT

❶ Wet the sponge and squeeze it to remove excess water.

❷ Squeeze several drops of food coloring on the brush to make 3 vertical rows (red, yellow and blue).

❸ Paint with the sponge on a large sheet of paper to create Rainbow Paint pictures.

PROJECT TIPS & IDEAS

✓ Try different color schemes by dripping other colors on the brush.

✓ Make banners for school or special events.

Lava Lamp in a Jar

It's groovy to watch the colored blobs rise and fall.

WHAT YOU WILL NEED

Plastic jar

Water

4 drops food coloring

Table salt

Vegetable oil

HOW TO MAKE IT

❶ Fill the jar 3/4 full with water. Add 4 drops of food coloring and stir.

❷ Slowly pour 1/3 cup of vegetable oil on top of the water. Wait 5 minutes or until the layers of liquid are settled.

❸ Sprinkle salt on top of the oil until the oil and salt form a blob that sinks to the bottom of the jar.

❹ As the salt dissolves, the oil will float back to the top. Add more salt to create more diving blobs. This creates the illusion of a lava lamp.

PROJECT TIPS & IDEAS

✓ Try creating several Lava Lamps in different colors.

✓ Experiment by using rock salt and see how it reacts compared to the table salt.

The Best Play Dough

Make a super smooth, easy-to-knead dough.

WHAT YOU WILL NEED

2 cups flour

2 cups water colored with 1/2 tsp. food coloring

1 cup salt

2 tbs. vegetable oil

1 tbs. cream of tartar

HOW TO MAKE IT

❶ Mix all ingredients in a pot and cook over medium heat while constantly stirring.

❷ Continue to stir for 4-5 minutes or until the mixture turns into dough.

❸ Remove from heat and allow the mixture to cool for 10 minutes.

❹ Remove the dough from the pot and knead it on waxed paper for 3-4 minutes.

❺ Store in an airtight container or ziplock bag.

❻ Repeat the steps above to create dough in various colors.

PROJECTS TIPS & IDEAS

✓ Dough will last longer if stored in the refrigerator.

✓ Knead in 1 Tbs. glitter to create glitter dough.

Measurement Conversion

U.S.	METRIC
1/4 teaspoon	1 ml
1/2 teaspoon	2 ml
1 teaspoon	5 ml
1 tablespoon	15 ml
1/4 cup	50 ml
1/3 cup	75 ml
1/2 cup	125 ml
2/3 cup	150 ml
3/4 cup	175 ml
1 cup	250 ml

Food Coloring Blending

COLORS	FOOD COLORING
TEAL	3 drops blue + 2 drops green
ORANGE	3 drops yellow + 1 drop red
PURPLE	3 drops red + 2 drops blue
LIGHT GREEN	3 drops green + 1 drop yellow
DARK RED	3 drops red + 1 drop blue
GOLD	4 drops yellow + 1 drop red